A HISTORY OF PARKSIDE HOSPITAL MACCLESFIELD 1871-1996

A SENSE OF PERSPECTIVE

David A Broadhurst

Churnet Valley Books

Published by

CHURNET VALLEY BOOKS

43 Bath Street
Leek
Staffordshire
01538 399033

© David A Broadhurst and Churnet Valley Books
1997

ISBN 1897949 28 6

Reprinted 2016

Acknowledgements

I would like to thank the staff at the Macclesfield Public Library, Cheshire Record Office, Chester, Staffordshire Record Office, Stafford and the Postgraduate Medical library, East Cheshire NHS Trust, who have all been most helpful and patient.

Special thanks to Linda Wilkinson for the initial typing of the draft copy and Ian Menzies for his scanning expertise.

Thanks to Chris Dakin, formerly of the Works Department at Parkside, and to David Jackson for access to plans and maps of the site.

I am deeply grateful for the knowledge shared with me in my conversations with Dr.J.Littlewood, former Medical Superintendent, and Mr Norman Buckley, Mr E. Proctor, Mrs P. Butler, Mrs V .Perkins, Mr B. Perkins, Mr D. Whyte and Mrs M. Davison, whose memories of the hospital go back many years. Many of them have kindly loaned me photographs. Thanks also to Mrs Whittaker, Mr A. Stubbs, Miss M. McMahon, Mr E. Sherratt, Mr R. Patterson and Mrs A. Cockayne who have also loaned me photographs and certificates. Mrs A. Grundy and Mr D.Whyte have been most helpful in contacting other people with photographic material.

My many thanks are also due to all the other countless people, nursing staff, artisans, ex-administrators, patients, their relatives and friends who have contributed to this book and shared their recollections at what was a sad time, with closure imminent.

Last but not least I thank my wife and family who have given me every encouragement with the project, assisting with note-taking, photography and computer work. I must make special mention of my wife Ann's rescue of the Dovecote from demolition; she was luckily on site when it was about to be removed by the contractors!

David Broadhurst
Macclesfield, 1996

"The nomenclature and nosology of psychiatry still lack standardisation, concepts of aetiology are tentative, often contradictory and treatment is largely empirical. In practical terms therefore, it follows that we cannot yet afford to overlook any information which can be derived from historical sources about the management in the past of those problems that still perplex us at the present day."

William Parry-Jones
Lecturer in Psychiatry
University of Oxford

Foreword

I have for some years thought that someone should write the history of Parkside Hospital before it becomes impossible because of the scattering or destruction of records. Momentarily I contemplated doing it myself but rapidly discarded the idea when I realised the huge amount of work involved in such a project.

Fortunately, David Broadhurst was not as easily deterred as myself and has now completed his self imposed task. I think this book is an important contribution to those areas of historical knowledge all rather thinly covered previously.

Firstly, of course, there is the history of the hospital itself. I found this fascinating and in parts quite surprising. During my time as a consultant there I thought we were the best psychiatric hospital in the Country but imagined that in other times, particularly perhaps in the years before the Second World War, the hospital was something of a backwater. I was obviously entirely wrong and it is clear that at the time the hospital was amongst the leaders in occupational, social and recreational therapies. This account of the hospital also includes information on a remarkable variety of topics including, for instance, the construction of the hospital clock, the local bird life and guidance to the hospital architecture.

Secondly, it covers the development of services for the mentally ill from the stage of the workhouses and private madhouses upto the very present, characterised mainly by small units in association with general hospitals and the gradual, and at times hesitant, evolution of treatment in psychiatry. Again I found much of this surprising; for instance, one likes to think of light therapy for seasonal affective disorder as a recent development, whereas it is clear that this was in use before the Second World War.

Lastly this book is a notable contribution to the local history of the area as Parkside was for many years one of the largest employers in Macclesfield and must have made a major contribution to the prosperity of the town and influenced its development. This concentration of hospital services in the town has given rise to a tradition of nursing in many local families producing a loyal, caring and devoted professional workforce.

We are perhaps still too close in time to the demise of the county mental hospitals to properly evaluate them. It is sad that in their latter years they were subjected to the sort of denigration described by the author. No doubt some aspects of the regime were bad, but there was much that was good. In my present work I spend much time visiting other psychiatric units and talking to patients. I usually enquire about what they do during the day in the ward and too often the answer is "lying on my bed", or "smoking", or "watching the television" or some combination of these activities. I think people are more contented when they are busy and this level of inactivity cannot be beneficial. In the past there probably was an element of exploitation and indeed, I remember early in my psychiatric career, seeing a group of patients walking in lines across a field picking up stones. This was at another hospital and I doubt whether this sort of mindless activity would ever have been tolerated at Parkside and it was soon abolished in all hospitals. Those patients who worked on the wards would talk about their work with pride and it clearly gave them a sense of some personal worth. Certainly the remarkable variety of activities described by the author available at Parkside would have left little time for regressive introspection.

I think this book is an important step in the process of restoring a balance in the historical assessment of the county mental hospitals and I am sure it will be of great interest to those of us who worked in them as well as to the local historians and as an account of the general development of psychiatric treatments.

Dr M.S.Bethell, MA, MB, Ch B FRC Psych
Consultant Psychiatrist
September 1996

4

Contents

Main Entrance, Admission Hospital, Annexe
From 1920-1950 the Annexe Laboratory on the second floor of the building was the main provider of laboratory services for the Macclesfield District. The car is a Flying Standard.

Introduction

With the closure of Parkside Hospital due to take place in 1996/97, and in response to requests from staff, patients and the general public, I have endeavoured to compile a brief history of Parkside, linked closely with the contemporary medical and social developments in such hospitals. Most large mental hospitals were run on very similar lines to Parkside and were built during the Victorian era when the law obliged each county to provide asylum care for the mentally ill. Then, from the early twentieth century, there was a growing belief that mental illness was treatable. This book traces the changes through the years, incorporating the history of Parkside based on thorough research, to give the reader an understanding of the key developments in the treatment of mental illness.

Trying to condense 125 years of caring and history into a book of this size has been difficult and worthy of a greater tome, so of necessity only the main developments have been included. However, I hope it will serve to demonstrate the historical importance of one of the largest public institutions in Macclesfield and the commitment of care and devotion by the staff over the years. Sadly, due no doubt to the social stigma attached to mental illness, little has been written about Parkside in local history circles. The subject is skirted around out of fear and ignorance, yet Parkside became the largest public institution in Macclesfield. Thankfully public attitudes towards mental illness are changing and a more enlightened and accepting era is emerging.

The part that Parkside has played both at county level and locally in Macclesfield is immense. The number of patients that have passed through Parkside Hospital from Cheshire and the surrounding counties amounts to many thousands. Between 1901 and 1947 the total number of patients receiving treatment amounted to 68,239. In the early days a number of patients in the hospital came from other areas outside the recognised catchment area and Parkside received a payment from the referring authority to care for them.

The retraction of the hospital has been going on for some time; brought about mainly by modern treatment methods and successive re-organisations of the health and local authority boundaries, both at local and regional levels, which have resulted in a big reduction in the catchment area.

A continuing social barrier to progress in the treatment of the mentally ill has always been our reluctance to accept and understand them. We have tended to socially isolate them. The words 'mad', 'crazy', 'asylum' and 'lunatic' are still very much in common usage and often used in a derogatory and derisory manner. A gradual change towards integrating the mentally ill more into the community, with the same rights, choices, benefits and comforts that we all enjoy, is taking place. Better understanding as to what constitutes good mental health is also playing a part. As a result of the pharmacological advances over the past forty years, the growing public awareness of mental illness, a reduction in the catchment areas and new methods of funding, the large mental hospitals have now outlived their usefulness and are being scaled down to a handful of wards and departments.

The closure programme to run down the large county mental hospitals was conceived in

1961 and subsequently accelerated from 1980 onwards. There were about 160 such institutions in the country at that time. By the end of the century well over half of these will have gone. The amount of thought, skill and energy that has been bound up in the planning, building and running of these hospitals is incalculable. Such an industrious and humanitarian era may never be repeated again.

Parkside has been one of the main employers in Macclesfield over the years. The number of nurses and doctors from this country and abroad that received their training at Parkside is vast. Many of these took up posts of responsibility throughout the world. Parkside became recognised internationally as a treatment and training centre of excellence. It was one of the first hospitals in the country to have any form of accredited training for nurses. Accounts of the hospital from 1871 to the early 1970s show us that the Medical Superintendents were enlightened and progressive in their thinking. Indeed in the early days, each doctor employed, including junior doctors, was expected to carry out a research project. The hospital was amongst the forerunners in the research of mental illness.

Occupational, social and recreational therapy, and subsequent rehabilitation, played a large part in treatment well before the introduction of pharmacological methods in the 1950s. In 1932 the World Health Congress held an exhibition in London and Parkside staged an exhibit stressing the importance of occupational therapy in the treatment regime. It was probably the first mental hospital in the British Isles to appoint a full time Occupational Therapy Officer in 1923 and has always been at the forefront of developments in this method of treatment, receiving international acclaim for its progressive thinking. Workers at Parkside realised early on the importance of occupying people suffering from major mental illnesses, concluding that a reduction in the amount of time spent doing nothing led to a significant improvement in the patient's condition, particularly in schizophrenia. To this day, occupational, social and recreational therapies remain most important lines of treatment along with modern medication: both play their role towards recovery.

With the introduction of the phenothiazines in the 1950s, a major turning point was reached in the treatment of mental illness, followed by the antidepressants in the 1960s. The patient's distress and suffering was much relieved, bringing about a gradual return to normality for many people. Abnormal perceptions, thoughts and feelings were subdued and the patient became much more accessible and amenable, with a much greater response to occupational, social and recreational measures. Large numbers of people returned home to resume a more purposeful way of life or attended specialised rehabilitation centres throughout the country. Many of these centres offered craft apprenticeship courses, City and Guilds qualifications and basic literacy classes. The local branch of the Workers' Educational Association held lectures for patients in the Annexe for many years.

The sense of belonging and of identity and the community spirit were high during those exciting years of development, amongst both patients and staff. The hospital had its own football, cricket and other sports teams. It boasted its own orchestra, picture house, indoor and outdoor swimming pools and gymnasium. At one stage it became completely self sufficient having extensive market gardens, orchards and five farms. It brewed its own beer, baked bread and had its own Fire Brigade. Inter-hospital sports competitions were keenly pursued throughout Cheshire and neighbouring counties. A 'silent success story' has been going on at Parkside ever since its inception in 1871, moving forward with the latest developments, treatments and ideas. It has an enviable track record for successfully treating and caring for the mentally ill, both in the hospital and the community.

Throughout this book the terms 'occupational', 'recreational' and 'social' therapy have been used in their broadest senses to include any positive practical interaction with the patient. This would cover supportive psychotherapy, self-help skills, counselling, anxiety management, behavioural therapies and talking therapy. Terminology changes with time but the bedrock of treatment - care and rehabilitation - remain the same. The historical developments with the biggest impact in practical terms have been adhered to, rather than attempting detailed analyses of the plethora of recommendations and reports over the years.

Although modern pharmacological methods of treatment have greatly improved the prognosis of severe mental illness (schizophrenia, manic depressive psychosis, clinical depression and organic psychoses), they need to be combined with occupational, recreational, social and, if applicable, work therapy, in order to consolidate and aid a more effective and long lasting recovery. Efforts of self help on the part of the patient must always be rewarded. This line also applies to less severe illnesses - neuroses and other psychological problems as opposed to the psychoses. Indeed, in some cases introspective and self analytical treatments only serve to reinforce the condition and can be likened to keeping a wound open; not allowing it to heal. Such measures should only be used in the initial stages of the illness to abreact a particular problem and simply realising that a problem exists could actually solve it. Having identified the cause of the patient's unhappiness, guidelines for treatment, using more practical methods, must be formulated in order to enable acceptance and resolution to take place.

With regards to many modern day neuroses and psychological problems it may be true to say that there are more people ill because they are unhappy than there are people unhappy because they are ill.

David A Broadhurst

To judge rightly of the present we must oppose it to the past; for all judgement is comparative, and of the future nothing can be known. The present state of things is the consequence of the former, and it is natural to enquire what were the sources of the good that we enjoy, or of the evil that we suffer. If we act only for ourselves, to neglect the study of history is not prudent: if we are entrusted with the care of others, it is not just.

Samuel Johnson, Rasselas.

Chester County Lunatic Asylum. The first County Asylum for Cheshire built in 1829 to the designs of William Cole.

West Park Hospital, Prestbury Road. Formerly the Union Workhouse built to the designs of Scott and Moffatt in 1843-45

CHAPTER 1
Legislation and Administration

By the start of the eighteenth century a system of poor relief was established, having started in the late sixteenth century by the passing of two acts in 1597 and 1601. The Poor Law was based on the parish as the unit of administration. Each parish was under the control of the church wardens and had either two or four overseers of the poor working on a voluntary basis collecting the parish poor rate of 2d from each member of the parish. The proceeds were used for the relief of poverty. The Justices of the Peace in each county supervised the overseers. "Outdoor relief" in the form of small pensions, grants and loans was provided to the sick and aged poor. Orphaned and poor children were apprenticed to a craft, foster parents having been paid to look after them.

It became apparent over the years that the parish unit could not generate enough poor rate to cope with high rises of unemployment, increases in the prices of foodstuffs and the move from a rural to an industrialised community, bringing about a lowering of wages in some occupations. In 1782, Gilberts Act was passed and recognised some of these deficiencies, allowing parishes to group into Unions for the purpose of the Poor Law and to run workhouses jointly. The most difficult group to deal with was 'the able bodied', or 'unemployed' and these were usually sent to workhouses. This was called 'indoor relief'. Money was used to provide raw materials for unemployed adults to work within workhouses.

Following a Royal Commission in 1832 on the Poor Law, the Poor Law Amendment Act of 1834 was passed. This stated that there was to be no outdoor relief for the able bodied poor. These would be relieved in workhouses. The workhouses would be deliberately run to make them less attractive, with poorer conditions than those of poorly paid labourers outside. Discipline was harsh and diet poor. It was derived to drive the 'idle' to work. Each group of Unions had a workhouse run by a Board of Guardians, consisting of local and elected representatives, who in turn were supervised by three Poor Law Commissioners with headquarters at Somerset House.

The Poor Law framework was replaced in 1847 by the Poor Law Board, the president of whom was a Minister of the Crown and sat in Parliament, but the New Poor Law remained unchanged until after the First World War. In Macclesfield the Poor Laws were administered by the Macclesfield Union, run by the local Board of Guardians and in 1848 a new workhouse opened on Prestbury Road. It was built in 1843-45 by the famous architects Scott and Moffat in the Tudor style. It now forms part of West Park Hospital, being a Grade II listed building. The main form of work provided was stone breaking and oust picking.

As the nineteenth century progressed, social reformers became greatly concerned at the large number of mentally ill people still in workhouses. Medieval Europe had left the treatment of the mentally ill to priests and superstitious witchcraft. In 1816 a committee was appointed to look into the conditions in the 'madhouses' in England. They found a greater number of persons than had been estimated, too much restraint, insufficient staff, inefficient inspection and faulty receiving certificates. At York Lunatic Asylum it was found that there had been great neglect and cruelty. When the Superintendent of Bethlem Hospital was questioned about the treatment of his patients he said *'Patients are ordered to be bled about the latter end of May, according to the weather. After they have been bled they take vomits once a week for a certain number of weeks. After that we purge the patients. That has been the practice for years, long before my time'*. Patients were chained in states of nudity to tables. A female patient in a hospital at Bethnal Green was kept in a quondam pigsty and immorality and depravity were rife.

Wynn's Act was introduced in 1808 with the purpose of providing 'better care' and the maintenance of lunatics being paupers or criminals in England. Further amendments to this Act followed in 1811 when the county rate was raised in order to build more asylums. In 1842 the Metropolitan Commissioners inspected all institutions and further legislation came about with the passing of the Lunacy Act of 1845. Permanent Lunacy Commissioners or inspecting authorities for the whole of the country were appointed and each county had to provide asylum care for the mentally ill. Prior to this the Select Committee report of 1827 had laid down that there must be a resident Medical Officer per 100 patients and restraint must only be used on the instruction of a physician, surgeon or apothecary. Great emphasis was placed on the keeping of proper records and each house, hospital or asylum visited four times a year by two persons and a medical visitor who reported to the Home Department.

Nottingham was perhaps the first of the new County Asylums to be built, taking in patients in 1811. Bedford followed in 1812, then Norfolk in 1814 and by 1827 there were Lancaster (170 beds), Stafford (120 beds), West Riding (250 beds), Cornwall (102 beds), Lincoln (150 beds) and Gloucester (120 beds). Before the passing of the 1845 Act all these were inspected by the local Justices. Between 1827 and 1845 eight more county asylums had been built; these included Middlesex, Dorset, Kent, Norfolk, Suffolk, Leicester, Surrey and Chester in 1829 with 90 beds.

The introduction of the great non-restraint movement between 1838-1848 marked an important turning point in the history of treating the mentally ill. It was pioneered by Robert Gardiner Hill (1811-1878) and John Connolly (1794-1866) and with it came the early beginnings of the modern mental hospital and later the recommendations that no more than 200-250 patients should be housed in any one asylum, a recommendation which in practice proved impossible during later years. In "A Concise History of the Entire Abolition of Mechanical Restraint and of the Non-Restraint System, 1857", during the writing of which Gardiner Hill actually lived with the patients and studied their habits whilst working at the Lincoln Asylum as the House Surgeon, he deduced that: *'with suitable buildings and a proper system of surveillance, instrumental restraint was unnecessary and injurious.'*

Likewise John Connolly, after taking over the largest asylum in the country, the Middlesex County Lunatic Asylum at Hanwell on 1st June 1839, abolished every form of personal restraint within the first four months of his appointment. Coercion chairs, handcuffs, strait-waistcoats and leg locks were entirely removed from the wards. This was the start of a more humanistic and scientific approach, which gained greater momentum during the last quarter of the 19th century.

By the time Parkside Hospital was built most forms of mechanical restraint such as coercion chairs, leg locks and other types of ironmongery had long gone. Linen jackets with buttons down the back and long sleeves with tapes on the ends remained. The patients' arms would be folded across the chest and the sleeves fastened behind the back with the tapes. Gloves without fingers, fastened at the wrists with buttons or locks were also used. Restraint was only used as a last resort and to prevent self injury or to stop the patient from removing dressings from wounds. The Parkside records indicate that gloves without fingers were probably the most widely used form of restraint, This was only necessary for a small number of patients as the records amply demonstrate and each one had to be witnessed by the Medical Superintendent.

During 1876 Parliament passed a law granting four shillings a week from government funds for the maintenance of pauper lunatics. This induced some parochial authorities to categorise poor people as lunatics, forcing them into asylums, in order to obtain the government grant! Great efforts followed over the years to improve the treatment of the mentally ill and the passing of the Lunacy Act of 1890 helped to remedy some of the deficiencies. The Act set out how the County Asylums should be run with the appointment of Visiting Committees as governors to inspect the hospitals five times per year. The Act also made the large County Asylums liable to pay rates. Despite the 1890 Act, supervision was still insufficient and many people were detained unjustly and wrongly. By the close of the nineteenth century there were only ten Commissioners in Lunacy to watch over the interests of an estimated 106,611 patients in asylums scattered throughout England and Wales. These included private asylums, state asylums, workhouses and private homes.

It is of interest to note that the term 'Asylum' was adopted by several institutions and became very fashionable at the time, usually denoting a new extension to Lunatic Hospitals, as later did the term 'Annexe' in the early 1900s. The term also means 'a place of refuge', which indeed they became for many a poor tormented soul rejected by society.

The Lunatic Hospital at Manchester was attached to the Infirmary in 1765 and the two combined became known as the Manchester Infirmary and Lunatic Hospital. This was to become the model for many future provincial asylums to be attached to general hospitals. Due to increasing specialisation the mental illness side eventually became separate with a new hospital built at Cheadle. Before the large County Asylums were built there were numerous private asylums, small group houses and homes for the mentally ill. The first private asylum was built by Anthony Addington (1713-1790) MD Oxon, FRCP, at Reading in Berkshire in 1749. The mid-20th century saw the building of Psychiatric Units as separate entities away from the large County Mental Hospitals and this was to change yet again when it became fashionable to attach Psychiatric Units to District General Hospitals. A recent government report continues the argument and questions the therapeutic suitability of even having separate mental health units within District General Hospitals.

In the nineteenth century the fear of being put into an asylum was very great. Many people were wrongly certified and carried off to the County Asylum. In 1869 the Reverend William O'Connor became involved in a mild fracas in a shop and, at the instigation of the Chief Constable of Manchester, was whisked away to Prestwich Asylum, despite much protestation by Mrs O'Connor. He was discharged three days later when it was realised that a mistake had been made. A Mrs Petschler was committed to Altrincham Workhouse by her sister for business reasons. Mrs Petschler's husband had died and she took over the running of his business, much to the annoyance of her sister. Her sister then arranged to have her certified by a clergyman and transferred to the Cheshire County Lunatic Asylum at Macclesfield. Following Mrs Petschler's discharge from the asylum it was found out that her home had been broken up and the property sold to pay for her treatment as a private patient; thus her sister's objective of destroying her business had been achieved. Mrs Petschler had no money to sue for damages and the clergyman could not be prosecuted under the law, even though a magistrate was available at the time of certification. The newspapers took up the case and brought to light other cases of wrongful committal.

Some asylums were bright and cheerful, but others were bleak, harsh and lacked diversional activities. At one asylum in 1882 the deceased insane were buried in unmarked graves, the final humiliation. Great stigma was attached to pauper funerals; the procession was not allowed to pass along the 'Queen's Highway', but had to use side roads. This state of affairs persisted until 1919. The reports of the Commissioners in Lunacy often made complaints about the state of the drains, the smells and the standards of hygiene and care. Macclesfield Asylum was not immune and during one year the Commissioners arrived to find a ward of thirty five patients without an attendant and one of the patients in a fit.

As discussed previously, many mentally ill, handicapped, epileptic and socially disadvantaged people would be found in the workhouses. Medical classification and diagnosis were fairly rudimentary and there was little understanding of the causation of the unusual behaviours manifested by these people. They tended to be classified as pauper lunatics, idiots and imbeciles. This classification lasted up to the late 1920s. With the arrival of a more scientific and humanistic approach towards the end of the late nineteenth century and the need to treat rather than detain, a more enlightened era began.

Not all mentally ill people were kept in the workhouses. Crowther states that *'the workhouse doctor was obliged to commit to any asylum any insane pauper who appeared dangerous, but with harmless causes'*. He would use his own judgement or bow to the wishes of Guardians who objected to the high cost of asylum treatment. The cost of 'indoor' maintenance in the workhouse per person per week could be sometimes half of the asylum charge, although this varied amongst the different asylums. Perhaps because of this financial disparity, many mentally ill people remained in workhouses. The mentally ill, handicapped and people suffering from epilepsy living in workhouses received regular visits from the Commissioners in Lunacy, although there would appear to have been very few special wards for them. The Lunacy Amendments Act of 1862 recommended that suitable accommodation for the mentally disabled be created in the workhouses, but in practice this never really got off the ground.

Other factors which probably had a bearing on lunacy legislation and the way workhouses and poor houses were administered were the Local Government Acts of 1888 and 1894 and these may well have caused some confusion until the changes were widely accepted and things settled down. The 1888 Act extended the principle of democratic control to smaller communities with the so called 'County Councils Act' of the Salisbury Government. This provided for the election of County Councils to take over the powers of local administration, formerly held by the Justices of the Peace at Quarter Sessions. Sixty towns were given greater independence with the status of County Boroughs. Previously a County Borough was a town with more than 50,000 inhabitants.

In 1894 the Liberals established urban and district councils within the counties, assigning to them questions of housing and sanitation. Also at that time parish councils were created within the rural districts for communities of more than 300 people.

The start of the 1900s saw an acceleration of general social changes, of pay and conditions of employment, with many new acts being passed. In 1903 at Parkside, Attendant Samuel Scragg, upon retiring due to ill-health, was granted £50 per year pension under the powers of the Lunacy Act of 1890, Sections 280 and 281. A move towards preventing poverty began with the introduction of old age pensions in 1908, the creation of unemployment exchanges in 1909 and the birth of National Insurance in 1911. At Parkside in 1908 the whole of the asylum staff were insured.

The workhouses became known as 'Institutions' in 1913 and the State Registration of Nurses took place in 1914. Further changes in pay and conditions started to take place. The Asylum Officer's Superannuation Act of 1909 came about and in 1917 the local branch of the National Asylum Workers Union at Parkside claimed a pay rise for male staff plus a war bonus. In 1920 the Pensions Increase Act was passed.

Gwendoline Ayers describes the Poor Law Medical Services as being the origin of the National Health Service. Infirmaries came about because of the inability of the voluntary sector to expand sufficiently to meet the needs of growing demand. Poor Law nurses cared for 75% of all hospital patients and by 1920 there were twice as many Poor Law nurses as in the voluntary sector. By this time the role of the large County Asylum had changed and every one was admitted and classified according to signs and symptoms, with a report each year by the Medical Superintendent. The population of Cheshire had increased threefold over eighty years and the number of hospital beds in the county thirty times. A change of name was thought appropriate and in 1920 the Cheshire County Lunatic Asylum was renamed the Cheshire County Mental Hospital. The Lunacy Act of 1890 was amended so that the words 'hospital' and 'patient' could be used throughout the country. The term 'mentally handicapped' was also adopted and the old classification of 'idiot' was discontinued. During 1913 the Lunacy Commission was reorganised and became known as the Board of Control, England and subsequently merged into the Ministry of Health as part of the 1959 Mental Health Act.

In 1929 the Local Government Act became law but the Poor Laws still persisted and were eventually absorbed by the Public Assistance Act. The workhouses then became known as Public Assistance Institutions, and Infirmaries were built or attached to the workhouses. The word 'institution' is now used in a disparaging manner and has gone out of fashion, but when first introduced it was accepted with enthusiasm. The Boards of Guardians were eventually abolished and their functions transferred to County Councils. Following the reforms of the post-war Labour government as a result of the Beveridge Report, the National Insurance Acts of 1946, the National Assistance Act of 1948 and the creation of the National Health Service in 1948 to take over the hospitals, the Poor Laws finally ended.

A major turning point was reached with the introduction of the Mental Treatment Act of 1930, providing for the voluntary and temporary reception of patients along with the establishment of outpatient clinics. This was a result of the advances since the turn of the century, and the recognition that treatment was possible rather than just detention and certification. Research was carried out on a variety of treatments at Parkside during the 1920s and 1930s.

Following the 1930 Act, the Duly Authorised Officer took patients to hospital but a Magistrate's signature was still required on the certification papers. Then followed the MWO, or Mental Welfare Officer, with a different approach and better training. Magistrates were eventually relieved of the duty of certification as they could not be expected to know much about mental illness, and the task was passed to doctors to certify against the patient's will.

The Health Service Act of 1948 ushered in the National Health Service to take over the hospitals, thus altering catchment areas and financial administration and at Parkside ending 77 years of administration at county level. During the immediate post-war years and following the introduction of the National Health Service, the cost per patient head dropped considerably and conditions generally were very austere until stability was achieved.

During 1954/57 the Percy Commission discerned that: *'public opinion in general was moving towards a more enlightened attitude which is fostered by the progress which has been made during the last fifty years in the understanding and treatment of mental disorders'*.

Percy pointed the way to a new emphasis on care and the breaking down of barriers between mentally ill and mentally handicapped people and the general population. This led the way to the Mental Health Act of 1959 and the word 'voluntary' changed to 'informal'.

Many more changes have taken place since then, bringing about further improvements in treatment but also putting more emphasis on community care, patients' rights, choices and needs, subsequently leading to the amendment of the 1959 Act and the passing of the 1983 Mental Health Act. The main aim of the 1983 Act was to safeguard the rights and protect the interests of the mentally ill subject to Mental Health Assessment. The Act afforded more protection to people with mental disorders regarding compulsory admission, detention and treatment.

In 1990 the National Health Service and Community Care Act came about. This put more emphasis on provision of care in the community in preference to hospital care. It stressed the inter-dependency of social care agencies and their need to work collaboratively. Through these provisions it was anticipated that an individual's needs for and choice of care in the community could be better met. The same Government White Paper, 'Caring for People', also introduced to the National Health Service, from April 1991, the concept of 'purchaser/provider' arrangements, along with new arrangements for Local Authorities from 1993. The start of a business culture began with unfamiliar words of 'purchaser', 'Hospital Trust', 'opting out', 'provider', 'budget-holding', 'indicative prescribing budget', 'Fundholding GP' and many others. Several successive 'waves' of NHS Hospital Trusts emerged throughout the country, run by their own board of directors, with the ability to own assets, borrow money, develop their own services and employ their own staff, ultimately becoming the 'providers' of health care services. The other half of the Health Authorities became separate and were known, alongside fundholding GPs, as the 'purchasers', buying in the requisite health care for their district from both NHS Trusts and the private sector.

The remaining long stay hospital population in the large psychiatric hospitals and younger patients requiring continuing care will be transferred by the Health Authority Purchasers under contractual agreements to smaller units scattered over a wider area and integrated more into the community. These will range from group homes of 4 to 8 patients to larger Nursing Home type provision with more specialised care by trained staff. The outcome of this widespread fragmentation of the mental health sector remains to be assessed by future historians. The latter reforms are based on providing people with long-term mental illness with the basic needs and civil rights which we all enjoy and fitting in with the way the NHS is funded, rather than advances in treatment as in previous Acts.

Administration

From 1871 to 1889 the hospital was supervised by a visiting Committee of Justices, appointed by the Court of Quarter Sessions. Following local government reforms by the Salisbury Government and in particular the 1888 Act which became known as the 'County Council Act', bringing about the election of county councils to take over local administration formerly held by Justices of the Peace, the hospital was taken over by Cheshire County Council. In 1889 they appointed a Committee of Visitors to oversee the running of the hospital and a subcommittee called the House Committee to exercise the day to day supervision of the hospital. This arrangement lasted for a further 58 years.

A new set of rules for the Government and Management of the Hospital were made in 1911. The previous rules had been made in 1871, with some slight modification up to 1886, so a 'Model Set of Rules' were implemented following recommendations made by the Commissioners in Lunacy. During 1921, due to advances in medical science and social changes, a revision of the name was felt appropriate, from the Cheshire County Asylum to the Cheshire County Mental Hospital. At this time the rateable value of the Main Building increased from £2,228 to £2,510 by agreement with the overseers of the Township of Macclesfield (the Lunacy Act of 1890 made it liable to rates). The average cost of maintenance in Public Institutions round about this time reads as follows for year ending 31st March 1919, from the Chancellor of the Exchequer's report:

Paupers in workhouses	20s 6d per week
Convicted prisoners	30s 10d per week
Convicts sentenced to penal servitude	42s 9d per week
Pauper lunatics in asylums	16s 8d per week

In 1940, due to further advances, a change of name from Cheshire County Mental Hospital to Parkside Hospital, Macclesfield, came about. The words 'county' and 'mental' were removed from the names of a large number of mental hospitals at that time and more so following the formation of the NHS in 1948, when the large mental hospitals ceased to be administered at County level. The word 'mental' was dropped to get away from the stigma in the popular mind.

The Upton Mental Hospital, near Chester, which was the original Chester Asylum, became known as Deva Hospital, Deva being the Roman name for Chester.

In 1948 the National Health Service took over, following a survey of the nation's hospitals in 1941 and wide cross-party parliamentary support for a national publicly-owned service giving free treatment to all out of national funds. The NHS hospitals were organised into regions and subdivided into 'Groups' with their own committees. Parkside became part of the Manchester Regional Health Board, but was still managed by its own Committee and financed separately from other Macclesfield Hospitals. Thus ended 77 years of administration at County level. In the 1950s Parkside amalgamated with West Park Hospital but was still financed separately and at that time was still the main provider of laboratory services. Publication of the long awaited Guillebaud report in 1956 remained in favour of mental hospitals being kept separate under their own management committee and not in combination with general hospitals.

Fourteen years later, in 1970, Parkside Hospital Management Committee was merged with Macclesfield and District Group Hospital Management Committee to form the East Cheshire Hospitals Management Committee, thus bringing all the hospitals in the Macclesfield and Congleton areas under the administration of a single authority. Up to that time all the large mental hospitals had remained free standing single unit groups under entirely different administrators and separately financed.

In 1974 the East Cheshire Hospital Management Committee moved from the control of Manchester Regional Health Authority to the Mersey Regional Health Authority. A much more significant National Health Service reform occurred in 1982, when Parkside became part of Macclesfield Health Authority and effectively ceased to have its own financial and administrative control, thus ending 110 years of independence. The Medical Superintendent's post was also abolished at this time.

Probably the most far reaching National Health Service reforms of late arose as a result of the Government White Paper, 'Caring for People'. This introduced to the National Health Service, from April 1991, the concept of Purchaser/Provider arrangements, along with new arrangements for local authorities from 1993. Parkside made a 'bid' to become part of a Community Health Unit Trust, but was not accepted by the Secretary of State. Following this it merged with the District General Hospital and is currently (November 1994) part of the 'Provider Unit' of the East Cheshire NHS Trust. In October 1992 a Business Manager was appointed at Parkside.

On 1st October 1993, Macclesfield Health Authority merged with Crewe District Health Authority and the two combined, becoming the South and East Cheshire Health Authority, representing the 'Purchasing' half of the reformed NHS, with its headquarters at Hartford near Northwich. It is currently (November 1994) in the North West Regional Health Authority, following the recent merger of Mersey and North West Regional Health Authorities. Ironically, following further mergers the Cheshire Health Authority 'Purchasers' have moved back to Chester. They are situated in the original 1829 Cheshire County Lunatic Asylum, where the mental illness branch of the Health Authority evolved. Yet another example of the wheel of history going full circle.

Inspections

Throughout its history Parkside has been subject to the prevailing legal requirements and inspections from the different governmental, local and statutory bodies. Under the requirements of the 1890 Lunacy Act, the Committee of Visitors had to visit and inspect the hospital five times per year.

The Commissioners in Lunacy, later the Board of Control and currently the Mental Health Act Commissioners, have been the main external body who visit Mental Hospitals, carrying out detailed inspections and submitting their findings in the form of a report and recommendations to the Hospital Management Committee.

Representatives from the Board of Guardians for each Union also visited the hospital on a yearly basis, to ensure that proper conditions and care were accorded to the patients from their Unions. In 1929 a Local Government Act made County or Borough Councils establish the Public Assistance Committees. They took over from the Board of Guardians, with the reports and recommendations coming from the Public Assistance Boards. Modern day Community Health Councils probably carry out a similar role today.

Following the First World War, annual visits began by an Inspector from the Ministry of Pensions for Service Patients, again to ensure that all Service patients within the hospital received proper care and attention. Reports were submitted following each visit and recommendations made to the Committee. At this time Service patients were classed as private patients and when, in 1923, nine service patients at Parkside were transferred to the pauper class by the Ministry of Pensions this caused much indignation in the local press.

In 1925 overcrowding at Parkside was particularly bad, so the Board of Control recommended that temporary overcrowding be relieved by discharging patients into the care and custody of relatives and friends, under the provisions of the Lunacy Act of 1890, Section 79, and this in fact started to take place.

Other bodies carrying out inspections every so many years have included the Royal College of Psychiatrists and inspectors from councils and boards of nursing to assess the suitability of the hospital to carry out Doctor and Nurse training, although with the gradual closure of the large mental hospitals, following the most recent health service reforms, their role is becoming increasingly unclear in practice.

Since the relaxing of crown immunity from NHS property, other bodies and organisations are playing a more prominent role, such as the local Environmental Health Department, Health and Safety Inspectorate and the ever increasing European regulations.

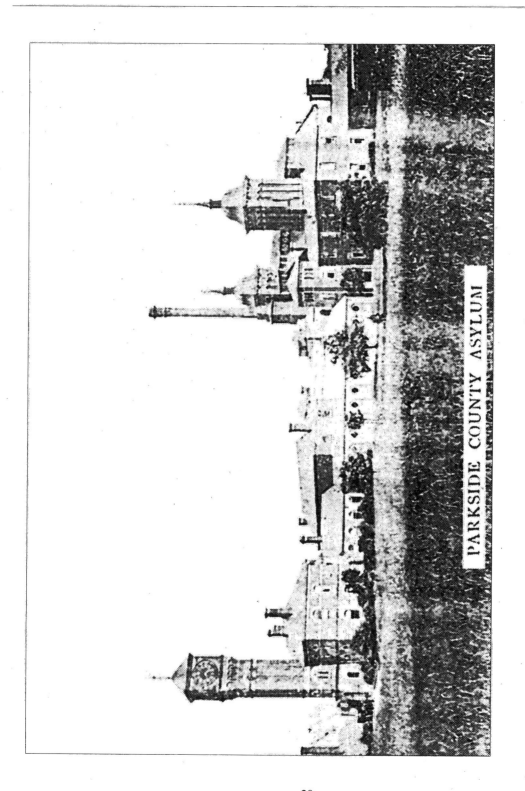

PARKSIDE COUNTY ASYLUM

View of the hospital before the Female Epileptic Block was built between the clock tower and the laundry in 1891

CHAPTER 2
A Sense of Perspective

In order to maintain a sense of perspective and to oppose the widespread simplistic misconceptions of the large mental hospitals, it must not be forgotten that a considerable number of people in mental hospitals during the early years and indeed even up to the Second World War, suffered from physical illnesses, infectious diseases, epilepsy and undiagnosed toxic and febrile states. The main drug groups had yet to be synthesised. The incidence of 'gaol fever' and 'hospital fever' has been well documented and the likelihood of a person in one of these institutions contracting an infectious disease was very high. At Parkside, the Main Building housed two infirmaries or sick wards, both two-storeyed and likewise when the Admission/Infirmary Hospital known as the Annexe opened in 1905, it too had several sick and infirm wards and blocks for patients suffering from chest diseases, particularly tuberculosis. The Parkside Isolation or Fever Hospital (now demolished) opened in 1896 on the other side of Victoria Road, where the East Cheshire Hospice now stands and was used for infectious diseases. Following the recommendations made by the Commissioners of the Board of Control in 1919, the County Architect, Mr Harry Beswick, drew up plans for the building of a detached infirmary hospital next to the Isolation Hospital, away from the general wards. This consisted of a general hospital block, two blocks for tuberculosis patients and the conversion of the Isolation Hospital into a colitis block. This in fact never took place and was abandoned due to what was termed 'financial stress'and instead the numerous verandah extensions to the wards took place during the 1920s.

Many isolation hospitals, sanatoria and asylums were built out in the countryside. There were several reasons for this. In the case of the mentally ill one reason was because the workhouses were unable to cope with their behaviour and the more pronounced cases were very often removed and left to wander about, becoming the object of ridicule and amusement. So, to prevent people making fun of them and leering at them, they were segregated in large institutions out in the countryside. Another reason was to provide treatment and care in surroundings where the air was fresher than that of the industrial towns. Fresh air, exercise and outdoor sports were regarded as important adjuncts towards good mental and physical health. With adequate amounts of sunlight, a balanced diet and pleasant surroundings, the bodies' resistance to disease improved and anxiety was lessened. Treatments were based on restoring a balanced lifestyle based on a mix of occupational, recreational and social activities. This also fostered a sense of achievement and of community spirit. Confidence, self esteem and social awareness became more evident in the patients' behaviour over time. The likelihood of employment on the staff was much enhanced if one could play a musical instrument and participate in sport. A fit, healthy, mentally active workforce tended to emerge and this was reflected in the care given to patients. There may well be lessons in this for us today, with the emergence of campaigns to take more exercise and fresh air, leaving the car and a sedentary urban lifestyle behind. Many of the large mental hospitals were built in beautiful grounds and parkland, providing peace and quiet and a place to wander, so essential for well balanced mental health - another lesson for us to re-learn in these days of technological pressure, preoccupation with managerial/financial efficiency and growing urbanisation.

A beneficial effect that resulted later on, as a consequence of separating the mentally ill, mentally handicapped and epileptics into separate institutions, was growing specialisation, enabling greater understanding and investigation to take place into the causation of these three broad areas of mental disability. At the start of the 1900s, scientific research methods started to gain momentum. As a result Parkside became one of the most progressive and research minded hospitals in the country, particularly during the period from 1925 to 1940. Likewise, the David Lewis Centre for Epilepsy at Warford became the foremost treatment and research centre for epilepsy in the British Isles and remains so today. Also at Great Warford, South of Alderley Edge, another pioneer mental health worker, Miss Mary Dendy, developed the Sandlebridge Boarding Schools for mentally deficient children and later the mentally handicapped. She became the first woman Commissioner of the Board of Control following the Mental Deficiency Act of 1913. When she died in 1933 the Sandlebridge Boarding Schools were renamed the Mary Dendy Homes in her honour.

In 1918 Miss Dendy was one of the inspecting Commissioners of the Board of Control who carried out an inspection at Parkside. At this time infection was widespread throughout the hospital and the Committee had ordered that the toilet seats be removed in order to combat the spread of infection. On discovering this Miss Dendy advised that all the seats be put back immediately, much to the relief of all concerned.

As mentioned already, another group of people, who ended up in asylums were those suffering from different types of epilepsy. The bottom storey of the two storeyed block attached to the Main Building at Parkside, latterly Female 6/7 between the clock tower and laundry, was built specifically for people suffering from epilepsy and opened in 1891, as was Male 7 ward, between the clock tower and artisans yard, opening in 1903.

In 1904 the David Lewis Centre for Epilepsy was built, pioneered by a Victorian businessman and philanthropist, David Lewis (1822-1885), best known for his departmental stores in Manchester and Liverpool. The centre is situated three miles from Alderley, at Warford in the beautiful Cheshire countryside. It still maintains a village atmosphere with its half-timbered buildings set in 170 acres of parkland, and it remains the foremost treatment centre for epilepsy in the British Isles, incorporating established treatments and carrying out research work.

The Manchester Lunatic Asylum, built in 1765 at Piccadilly, Manchester, moved out into the countryside to Cheadle in 1848 and became known as Cheadle Royal Hospital, with thirty acres of meadows, eleven acres of arable land, two and a half acres of kitchen garden, five acres of flowers and shrubs and avenues with arbours providing shade. It still maintains this atmosphere to some extent and is largely run along traditional lines. With the formation of the NHS in 1948, it elected to remain private and is perhaps best known for its pioneering work in industrial therapy during the 1960s.

Why Parkside Hospital was Built

During the 1800s, asylum accommodation grew steadily. In 1827 there were only nine County Asylums, housing an average of 116 patients each. By 1910 there were 91 asylums, holding an average of 1072 patients each. The Vagrancy Act of 1744, the Private Madhouses Act of 1774 and the County Asylum Act of 1808 had addressed the problems of housing lunatics in separate accommodation in each county, but this was not compulsory. There were several private asylums in existence at that time. Following the Lunacy Act of 1845 it became compulsory for each county to provide an asylum for the mentally ill.

The Chester County Asylum at Upton, near Chester, gradually became overcrowded, with the annual admission rates rising steadily from 76 per annum in 1843 to 159 per annum in 1864. At a meeting on the 18th of July 1865, Dr Brushfield, Medical Superintendent of the Chester Lunatic Asylum, recommended increased accommodation for lunatic paupers in the County. In a subsequent report in which he noted the high price of land in the vicinity of Upton, it was decided to look elsewhere. On the 1st January 1866 the General Court of Quarter Sessions met in Chester Castle and decided to look for an eligible site for a new asylum for pauper lunatics from the North Eastern Unions of the County, viz Ashton-under-Lyne, Stockport, Altrincham, Congleton, Hayfield and Macclesfield. Sites were considered in Congleton, Knutsford, Stockport and Cheadle, but a site at Brickbank Farm, Henbury, along the current Pexhill Road, was chosen in December 1866. However, it was found that the terms were too circumscribed for additional land, and the Parkside site was chosen in Macclesfield. This came about largely due to the efforts of the Reverend J Thornycroft of Thornycroft Hall, Alderman Joseph Wright, the then Mayor of Macclesfield and Mr John May, a prominent and influential Macclesfield solicitor. The land was purchased by the County from the Governors of Macclesfield Grammar School for £10,562 15s, at the rate of £170 per acre on the south side of Boughey Lane, now called Victoria Road, on which the buildings stand, and £140 per acre for the portion on the north side. The County also redeemed the tithes on a portion of the land and purchased a water right flowing through their territory. The total area of land purchased came to 65 acres, 2 roods and 18 perches.

It was in 1848 that a Mr Jeremiah Clarke acquired a small house with four outbuildings and 11 acres of land situated in fields off Chester Road, opposite Ivy Road, beyond what is now a roundabout. He rented the property for £60 per annum from the Governors of Macclesfield Free Grammar School for the rest of his life. Little did he know that this site would one day become the Cheshire County Asylum. The smallholding was further developed into a farm and extended to 27 acres. When the County decided to buy the site in the mid-1860s for the new Asylum, Mr Clarke was served with notice to quit. The County were keen to acquire some of the fields in order that brick making could commence. He was getting on in years and did not want to leave and a lengthy correspondence ensued between the County, the Governors of the Grammar School and Mr Clarke's Solicitors from London. Eventually a sum was agreed upon and reluctantly Mr Clarke moved to Summer Hill further down Chester Road. The house which Mr Clarke vacated was called Parkside House, the colloquial name not officially adopted by the hospital until the 1940s. On some mid nineteenth century maps Parkside was written as two separate words, but the word Park and Side have gradually merged over time to become one.

Early Steps into the Community

Over recent years a perceived image has arisen amongst the layman, and even some modern health care reformers, regarding conditions in the large mental hospitals. The impression is that all patients were locked away, forgotten and subjected to various inhumanities. This image is untrue and does not reflect the real conditions, nor take into account the circumstances of the time. There is no doubt that some patients were subject to ill-treatment and others wrongly detained, but these represent only a small percentage. We must remember that the modern medication we take for granted these days was not available. There were no antibiotics, anti-psychotics, anti-tubercular or anticonvulsant drugs as we know them today. The task of nursing the mentally ill must have been enormous, but the records show that a considerable number of patients were treated successfully.

Parkside Hospital grew up during the latter years of the Victorian age. *"Notions of the Victorian era in the popular mind tend to be distorted and very often inaccurate,"* says Professor James Stevens Curl. *'Speeches of Politicians, utterances on radio and television and the offerings of journalists are peppered with references to the Victorian period, its values and buildings, that indicate widespread misconceptions, prejudice, ignorance and an almost incredible degree of warped perception. The adjective 'Victorian' is used in a derogatory manner to denounce hospital buildings that have become overcrowded, ham-fistedly altered, or not maintained, so that the Victorians are blamed for the shortcomings of more recent times."*

In 1895 Dr T.S.Sheldon, Medical Superintendent at Parkside, recommended that the *'asylum become more like a hospital than a place of restraint'*. He introduced band concerts, weekly dances and theatrical performances and started cricket matches which still continue to this day. By this time there were walking parties of 60-80 patients in the grounds, with 180 at weekends. Beyond the grounds there was a daily average of 50 patients. In the early days of walking parties beyond the grounds a London newspaper published an article criticising Parkside Hospital for allowing patients outside the perimeter of the hospital. The Medical Superintendent promptly replied by letter, stating: *'It is a pleasure to be able to record the humanity shown to our walking parties by farmers, cottagers and shop keepers'.*

The following brief extracts from the Committee's reports between the years 1890-1948 illustrate the gradual move from confinement in the wards to the outside community, despite very limited methods of treatment.

1890   583 patients in the hospital.

1895   Walking parties of 60-80 patients in grounds, 180 at weekends. Daily average of 50 beyond the grounds.

1903   Weekly fire drills, with surprise drill at 11pm.

1905   Only seven patients confined to airing courts for exercise.

1906   Patient numbers increased from 806 to 1026 following the opening of the Annexe.

1908   234 admissions in 1907. One staff to 9.7 patients.

1910   Patients' Fancy Dress Ball reported to be the most successful ever held.
         Main library and Annexe library restocked.

1913   Epileptics comprise 15% of the hospital population.

1916   1317 patients in the hospital, as follows: 1046 Cheshire pauper lunatics; 162 Out County (147 from Winwick Hospital which was used by the military); 109 Private.

1919   15.4% patients classed as epileptics.
1922   Parole had been allowed for male patients for many years, but the privilege allowed to female patients in 1922.
1923   Parole card system introduced and Male 10 Ward patients nursed on the 'open door system'.
        Front door and main gates also left unlocked.
        77 women allowed parole beyond the grounds.
        114 men allowed parole beyond the grounds.
        14 seater charabanc purchased 3/1/23 for private patients.
1925   Hospital encouraging discharge into the community to relatives and friends.
1926   Parole granted to 130 men and 60 women.
1929   Hospital authorities wrote letters to relatives and friends to encourage them to visit.
        101 patients on parole beyond the estate.
        4 female wards and 2 male wards using the 'open door system'.
1931   81 patients living apart from institutional care.
1948   196 patients allowed parole in grounds, 63 in town.

The start of the twentieth century saw a more understanding and humanistic approach gradually starting to take place, fuelled by scientific enquiry and medical research. Parkside kept abreast of all the latest developments and in some areas took the lead for the district. In 1920 a Clinical Laboratory was established and a visiting pathologist appointed. A further addition in this area occurred in 1924 when Dr E.S.Page, MRCS Eng, LRCP Lond, MB, BC Cantab, was appointed, with special experience in bacteriology and pathology. The Commissioners also reported in 1924 on the favourable addition of the laboratory for the hospital:

'We consider the new laboratory accommodation excellently adapted to the purpose for which it is intended and feeling as we do that much of the future advances in mental treatment and practically all advances in physical treatment, will depend upon scientific research, we regard the provision of these useful adjuncts as a valuable step in the right direction. On the grounds that many mental hospitals are now finding their laboratory provision of infinite value and that such facilities will become increasingly necessary, we hope the Committee will not shrink from incurring the expertise of appointing at an early date a full time Pathologist.'

At this time most specialists were visiting doctors, with no full time posts. In later years a full time Pathologist was appointed, Dr Stafford, who did some sterling work in the laboratory, providing the main laboratory service for the district, including GP and Infirmary services and this lasted up to 1950. During the Second World War the laboratory was upgraded to Area status and during 1942 a total of 4015 laboratory examinations were carried out. 1562 were internal, 1345 from outside the hospital and 1108 were from the Emergency Hospital in the Annexe.

In 1928 Dr Thomas Smith Harrison was appointed visiting Ophthalmic Surgeon and in 1932 Dr James Blair Hartley, MB BS Durham, DMME, was appointed Honorary Radiologist. Also in 1932, Dr Chevans, full time Medical Officer at Parkside wrote: *'Since the Mental Treatment Act of 1930 several patients have submitted themselves for treatment earlier than would have been the case had certification been necessary, so that the proportion of successful cases should tend to increase'.*

In 1932 Dr Chevans, was appointed Honorary Director of the new Manchester Children's

Guidance Clinic, a forerunner of Young People's Units.

'Down the road' at Macclesfield Infirmary, (now demolished) full time specialists began to be appointed in the early 1950s, with a full time Gynaecologist in 1952, followed by a Radiologist, Physician and Pathologist. In the late fifties the first hip joint replacements were done at the Infirmary. At Parkside neurosurgery was carried out at Cavendish Clinic, in collaboration with Manchester Royal Infirmary and in 1962 two full time Surgeons were appointed at the Infirmary. By this time a significant number of new drugs had been synthesised, marking a major turning point in the treatment of a wide variety of illnesses.

Research Studies

Between 1922 and up to the start of the Second World War in 1939 a considerable number of research studies were carried out at Parkside. Most of these were well documented and carried out over a period of years, many being published in the leading scientific and medical journals of the time including 'The Lancet' and the 'Journal of Mental Science'.

On 18th September 1925 the Macclesfield Board of Guardians inspected the hospital and the following extract from their report demonstrates the standing of the hospital at that time:

'We cannot speak too highly of the cleanliness and orderliness of the Institution and fully agree with The Lancet's comments of July last "That Parkside is one of the most up to date and progressive Institutions (Mental) in the kingdom"'.

A number of the studies involved the emerging treatments of light therapy, hydrotherapy, gland therapy and pharmacology. Others included dietary studies and a very extensive one was done on the incidence of tuberculosis at Parkside treating it with improved dietary methods, which brought about a greater resistance to the illness. Much attention has been given to diet over the years, with numerous changes, but the discovery of the accessory food factors in the mid-1920s marked a significant turning point. Opinions as to what constitutes a good diet have varied throughout history and no doubt will continue to do so. In one particular study at Parkside a small change in the diet effected a saving of £100 per year, indicating the cost-consciousness of pre-National Health Service days. Major studies were done into hereditary factors; one involving 1033 patients over a period of five years, in which all their living relatives were traced and questionnaires sent to them. Another study traced the case histories of 200 patients over a 25 year period. Follow up studies were also done on groups of patients following discharge to plot the progress of certain types of illness and again questionnaires were sent out, with a very good response rate.

When convulsion therapy first started to be used in the mid-1930s, with a drug called Cardiazol and later with Insulin, Dr Cormac toured the mental hospitals of Switzerland to study the methods being used, but he was not very impressed with what he saw. This was due to the poor research methods employed and the use of the treatment in different types of illness, giving very unclear results. 'The Lancet' later published an article which was very critical of its use. Modified electroconvulsive therapy, of course, came later and remains an important treatment for severe endogenous depression.

In many of the studies done, particularly light and hydrotherapy, staff volunteered to act as a control group. The benefits of sunlight were starting to be understood at that time and sunlight treatment rooms were attached to day rooms and dormitories. Many of the open verandahs were glassed in, these having been used previously for fresh air treatment of tuberculosis cases. The first hospital to use open air therapy in Britain was Baschurch Hospital in 1902. Sun treatment or heliotherapy. was essentially a Swiss method popularised by Dr Rollier of Leysin, who used sun baths in 1903. Workers at that time discovered that lack of sunshine could give rise to a depressed mood and reduced resistance to disease, especially tuberculosis and other infections. Of course, prolonged over exposure to sunlight can be damaging but once a protective tan is formed, or screening cream used, then this becomes less so.

Artificial light treatment or phototherapy was first used by Niels Finsen in 1894. He was later awarded the Nobel Prize for medicine in 1903 when he demonstrated that light treatment could be successfully used to treat tuberculosis of the skin. Light is essential for good mental and physical health. It plays a part in the formation of vitamin D, lowers blood pressure and improves the circulation. By acting on the pineal gland it regulates body rhythms, stabilises our moods, improves sleep, boosts the immune system and helps body growth and repair. Seasonal affective disorder causing lethargy, insomnia and depression during winter months affects over 10% of the population. Recent studies have shown that this disorder can be improved with light therapy. Spring daylight is especially beneficial. Modern urbanised ways of living in polluted cities and towns cuts out some of the essential light rays required by the body. In addition, working indoors, travelling everywhere by car, train or the underground deprives us of the light so necessary for good health. Certain types of eyewear including contact lenses also reduces essential light rays passing through the eyes. Further work on light treatment was done by Kromayer in 1904, using mercury vapour quartz lamps to produce ultra violet light and later on, in 1913, by Reyn, who added general irradiation to light treatment; by the use of carbon arc lamps. The ultraviolet rays produced chemical changes, helped kill germs and by acting on ergosterol contained in skin cells produced Vitamin D, so essential to bone growth.

Ultraviolet rays will not pass through conventional glazing made of soda glass, but will pass through boric glass which is more transparent, particularly if kept clean. As a result of this finding, vita glass hammocks were suspended in various parts of the grounds around the Annexe, both for treatment of physical disorders and diseases, and for mood disorders. Blood tests would be done following treatment. A superficial hyperaemia was produced with a better flow of lymph through ulcers and sinuses. The use of infra red rays followed later for the treatment of rheumatic conditions. Research work on light treatment continues today.

During the 20 year period between the two World Wars, Parkside's reputation as a progressive research and treatment centre steadily grew in Great Britain and abroad. Along with this, it became an excellent centre for the training of doctors and nurses, with direct benefit to the thousands of patients who have received care and treatment at the hospital.

In the early 1920s a series of monthly medical meetings began, to which were invited medical practitioners from the Cheshire area and doctors and senior nursing staff from Parkside. These were mainly held in the Annexe and created much interest amongst neighbouring mental hospitals. Below is a typical winter's session of lectures, indicating contemporary medical developments. Many of the lectures were given by visiting Professors or the medical staff from Parkside.

LECTURES

1927

October 19th	Encephalitis Lethargica by Dr D E Core, FRCP
	Post Encephalitic Cases by Dr Parkin
November 10th	Shock from an Experimentalist's Point of View by Dr A D MacDonald
	Endocrine Therapy by Dr L C F Chevens
December 14th	Mental Factors in General Medicine by Professor T H Pear, MA
	Insanities of Pregnancy and Parturition by Dr H D Cormac

1928

January 18th	The Physiological Basis Underlying Certain Mental Processes and Conditions by Dr H D Cormac
	Malarial Treatment of GPI by Dr L C F Chevens (Malarial treatment was first used at Parkside in December 1924)
February 15th	Intracranial Pressure by Professor J S B Stopford, MD
	Dementia Praecox by Dr L C F Chevens
March 14th	The Certification of Patients by Dr C Hubert Bond from the Board of Control
October 10th	The Cerebral Cortex by Professor McSwiney
	The Association of Some Abnormal Physical States with Vascular Uncontrol by Dr D E Core, FRCP
December 5th	Suicide and its Relation to Heredity and Mental Disorder by Dr L C F Chevens

1929

February 6th	The CerebroSpinal Fluid in Diagnosis by Dr H Stafford
March 6th	Cerebral Aneurysms by Professor J Shaw Dunn
March 12th	Actinotherapy in Mental Hospitals (this was a form of light treatment) by Dr H D Cormac
March 27th	The Important Part the Mind Plays in Ill Health by Professor G M Robinson, MD, FRCP (Edin)

It is recorded in the minutes of the Medical Superintendent's Report for 1928 that Parkside was one of the first mental hospitals to hold such lectures and meetings for general medical practitioners from outside the hospital.

Pharmacological Developments

In Victorian Britain one of the chief causes of death was lobar pneumonia. The scale of the problem can be likened to the current incidence of coronary artery disease. Diphtheria, scarlet fever and tuberculosis were rampant, along with dysentery and venereal disease. At Parkside in 1883, out of a total of 563 patients only 23 were taking any form of medication for either mental or physical illness.

The principles of vaccination had been discovered early on by Edward Jenner in 1795 and that was to lead to the immunisation of man against a number of diseases, but there was not the wide range of vaccines available then as there is today. Sir Almroth Wright (1861/1947) was later to introduce vaccination against typhoid fever to the British Army. Sir James Young Simpson (1811-1876) discovered chloroform on 15th November 1847, when he first used it for a surgical operation. Later Joseph Lister (1827-1912) discovered that carbolic acid kills germs and the principles of asepsis were born and Louis Pasteur (1822-1895) made the discovery of how germs were passed on.

The British Pharmacopoeia at the time of the outbreak of World War I listed only a handful of synthetic drugs including aspirin, introduced in 1889 and barbitone in 1903. The bulk of drugs were natural products like atropine from belladonna and morphine from the poppy. Gradually the isolation of the active chemical principles and pure substances came about when it was realised that the chances of therapeutic success were much greater than with the crude extracts from plants, which tended to vary with culture, soil and season. Thus the science of pharmaceutical chemistry was born during the last quarter of the nineteenth century and ultimately led to the rise of synthetic chemistry. Codeine was first isolated in 1832, followed by atropine in 1833 and papaverine in 1850. Many of these new discoveries were greeted with much scepticism and unfounded criticism and it was a very long time before pharmacological methods of treatment started to be accepted. Physiological methods were still preferred for many years. This line of thought probably came about as a result of post-mortem examinations, which revealed tuberculous cavities, necrotic tissue, empyemas, abscesses and cancerous or inflammatory processes of organs, which at that time would seem to be irreparable.

Towards the end of the nineteenth century and early twentieth century the casual organisms of infection and disease started to be identified. Treponema pallidum, the organism responsible for syphilis, was discovered by Schaudin in 1905 and following this a diagnostic blood test became available for syphilitic infection, named after its discoverer Wasserman, in 1907. Further advances in medical research started to take place. Insulin was first extracted from the pancreas in 1921; up to that time diabetes mellitus was a killer disease. The accessory food factors, or vitamins, started to be identified in 1926 and by the early 1930s the structures of the principal vitamins were established and much greater emphasis was put on dietary measures to combat a variety of disorders and diseases. Also at this time hormones were identified and the keystones of pharmacology, adrenaline, histamine and acetylcholine were recognised. Chromatography, ultra-centrifugation and electrophoresis started to be used in the 1930s and 1940s and the science of biochemistry evolved following the work of Fredrick Gowland Hopkins (1861-1947) on dietary needs.

Seven out of ten prescriptions written in the 1960s could not have been written in 1935; the medicines did not exist and there was no drug industry. The impetus for the sudden growth of the pharmaceutical industry was the introduction of the first sulphonamide in 1935. The discovery and action of this drug, a red dye called 'Prontosol' was credited to its discoverer, Dr Gerhard Domagk (1895/1964), for which he later received the Nobel Prize. It was the first drug to be completely effective against a germ inside the body and was used to treat puerperal sepsis, which had been a scourge of childbirth. It was later used to treat scarlet fever and erysipelas. Penicillin had earlier been discovered by Sir Alexander Fleming in 1928, but the work was abandoned because of problems with its purification and synthesis. This problem was later overcome by two American workers and it was used widely in trials by the army during the Second World War. Penicillin saved thousands of lives during the latter stages of the war.

By the end of the Second World War, public appreciation of science and medicine was much improved and food health policies came about along with a growing awareness of food hygiene methods. Penicillin was active against gram positive organisms and this was followed by Streptomycin, active against gram negative organisms and by the end of 1954 the incidence and death rate of tuberculosis had dropped dramatically. Further broad spectrum antibiotics began to be developed.

The 1950s saw a huge range of new drugs both for treating physical diseases as well as mental illness, epilepsy and behavioural problems. Post-war psychiatry gained perhaps its greatest impetus with the discovery of the phenothiazines, in particular chlorpromazine in the early 1950s. This set the stage for a whole range of neuroleptic agents, although to start with, like all changes, the new drugs were slow to be accepted and were not greeted with any real enthusiasm. Progress in psychiatry tends to be gradual as the approach is still largely along empirical and eclectic lines. Huge numbers of patients suffering from, or incapacitated by, schizophrenia were either discharged, or able to lead more purposeful lives, and the open door policy became the norm in the large County Mental Hospitals. The 1960s saw the introduction of the tricyclic antidepressants and for the first time there was an effective treatment for a large number of people in psychiatric hospitals with severe and crippling depression. The first compound used was imipramine, followed by similar drugs. Newer anticonvulsants started to be developed with carbamazepine in the early 1960s and sodium valporate, initially used in France and Italy, became available in England in the mid 1970s. Lithium carbonate had also arrived and provided a most valuable prophylactic drug in manic-depressive illness.

This combination of antibiotic, antipsychotic, anticonvulsant and antitubercular drugs, plus other pharmacological preparations for a variety of illnesses led to the large scale depletion of the long stay population in the large County Asylums. The need for admission was considerably reduced and people were treated as out patients in the community. By this time, in the 1950s, diagnostic techniques were also becoming more sophisticated and nurse training was undergoing a resurgence. Populations also started to decrease in general hospitals, sanatoria, convalescent homes and elderly care hospitals as a result of the new drugs. The 1970s saw depot injections being increasingly used and the formation of Community Psychiatric Nursing Services attached to the large mental hospitals.

Perhaps the benefits and the sense of security which modern medicine has brought sometimes lead to complacency as we forget all the discoveries and advances that have led up to the present day.

Vita glass hammock suspended
in grounds for sunlight
treatment, c1920

Hydrotherapy bath.

X-Ray Department

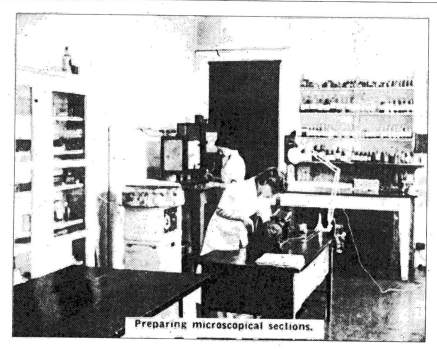

Inside the laboratory

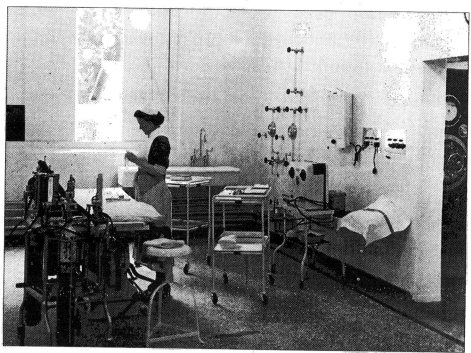

Part of the operating theatre, early 1950s.

Series of carbon arc lamps used for light therapy.

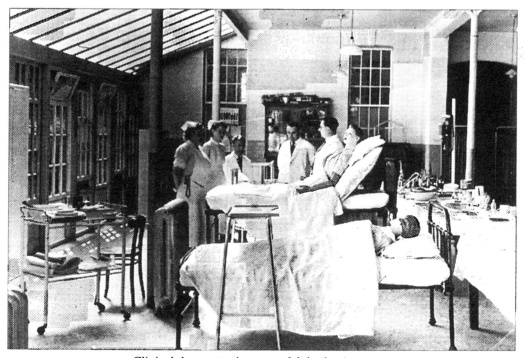

Clinical demonstration verandah in the Annexe.

Nursing staff in the day room of Female 3 Ward, Main Building, 1932.

CHAPTER 3
The Main Building, Water Supply and Church

The original principal hospital complex, referred to as the Main Building, was built between 1868 and 1871. It was designed and planned by the architect Robert Griffiths of Stafford. Funding was provided by Cheshire County, Birkenhead County Borough, and partly from Stockport County Borough. Its building came about as a result of overcrowding at Upton Asylum near Chester, also called Chester Asylum, which was originally built in 1829. The County decided to employ a reputable architect to construct a new County Asylum and the contract was awarded to Robert Griffiths, a significant architect who specialised in the building of hospitals, asylums and prisons. Griffiths was born in Broseley, Shropshire in 1825, the son of John Griffiths of Broseley. He was articled to Mr Pountney Smith, architect of Shrewsbury, but was unable to complete his apprenticeship owing to ill health caused by an incurable disease. Following this he was placed with his cousins Josiah and E.F.Griffiths, Quatford, Bridgnorth, Shropshire, who combined the business of architects and builders. At the age of 19, he supervised the building of Arley Castle. Shortly after, his cousins died, leaving him in charge; he later gave up the building side of the business in 1859 and in 1863 became County Surveyor of Staffordshire, a post which he held for 25 years.

Griffiths was responsible for the extension to Stafford Gaol and later became involved in the planning of extensions to Chester Castle, Beaumaris Gaol and Derby Gaol, but he was perhaps best known as the architect of a number of important asylums. His works include Herefordshire County Asylum in 1868 (£70,000 outlay), Macclesfield Asylum (later known as the New Cheshire County Asylum in 1868 (£120,000 outlay), Northamptonshire Asylum in 1873 (£600,000 outlay) and extensions to Stafford County Asylum in 1881, later called St George's (£45,000 outlay). He was also the architect of Shrewsbury Markets in 1885 (£23,000 outlay) and designed or restored several churches, including the restoration of St Chad's Church in Stafford, following the death of the eminent architect Sir Gilbert Scott. Work on private houses included the restoration of Seighford Hall near Stafford, a sketch of which appeared in the architectural room of the Royal Academy. One of his last designs was a spire for St Paul's Church, Forebridge, Staffordshire of which he was a church warden. In 1887, he was one of six architects selected to compete for one of the largest asylums in the country in Middlesex. A few weeks before his death he was selected to become President of the County Surveyors Society. He died on 29th May 1888 at his residence Highfield Grove, Stafford, aged 63 and is buried at Castle Church, Stafford.

Style
The style of architecture that Griffiths chose to use in the building of Macclesfield Asylum, later known as Parkside Hospital is essentially Italianate in the "Rundbogenstil" style, i.e. round-arched style. The term 'Italianate' indicates that a building is in the Italian manner usually because it has borrowed some of the features of Renaissance Italy. The 'Rundbogenstil' was a

35

term coined by the Germans during the latter years of Romantic Classicism and placed the stress on the use of an arch, whether appearing as an arcade or repeated fenestration. There are a number of arched curves including concave, convex, double curve and four-centred ogee, examples of which can be seen in the building at Parkside, with some particularly fine examples around the area of the clock tower. Each one of these arches would require the work of a skilled joiner to construct timber-form work for each arch, followed by the skills of the mason. The elements composing a typical arch are illustrated in the diagram.

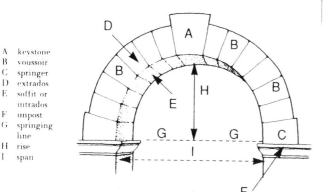

A   keystone
B   voussoir
C   springer
D   extrados
E   soffit or
    intrados
F   impost
G   springing
    line
H   rise
I   span

The Parkside building shows the fine use of polychrome brick with some interesting decorative features including corbelling, segmentally-headed window arches with varied-coloured voussoirs and key blocks. The entrance/administration block with central tower porch is particularly fine with a principal arched doorway of two orders, one and two-light windows to the lower two floors, a tall second bay with recessed round headed panels connected by impost band, the top most stage with the clocks to each face corbelled out and supporting a short spire.

Plan

The plan used by Griffiths was the block on pavilion type plan so often used at that time in the building of hospitals, asylums and prisons. Victorian public institutions tended to be orderly, logical, and grouped in blocks, particularly barracks, asylums, gaols and hospitals.

Block on pavilion plans arose because of a growing need for classification and early attempts to understand the nature of illness and diseases, particularly infections. The plan gave great emphasis to ventilation and light and the patients were grouped in the blocks according to their illnesses. The free circulation of air was encouraged by the use of open fireplaces, special ventilation ducts in the ceilings and even ventilation grills in the skirting boxes between individual beds. Upright flues in the external walls were also common and carried away the products of combustion from the fires and gas lighting along with the 'microbes' causing infection. Heating was provided by various warm water systems including the installation of heating coils under the floors and ducts in the walls, which served to improve the circulation of air. A close inspection of the remaining buildings at Parkside will reveal many of these features. All these arrangements were based on the best medical and engineering opinions of the time.

Blackburn Infirmary was perhaps the first hospital in England to be designed using the pavilion principle in 1858. The new St Thomas' Hospital between Westminster Bridge and Lambeth Palace, built during 1868-1871, is considered to be one of the finest of all pavilion hospitals, with eight four storey pavilions linked by corridors. The architect was Henry Currey (1820-1900), who designed many public buildings in the Italianate manner. By the 1870s and 1880s most newly built and renovated hospitals were using the pavilion plan and this persisted well into the twentieth century. In terms of initial cost it was expensive, along with maintenance, but it took into consideration the medical thinking and scientific opinions of the time.

Another hospital in Macclesfield built in the Italianate manner using the pavilion plan was Macclesfield Infirmary, 1867-1872 (now demolished). This was being built at the same time as Parkside. The architect was James Stevens, a local architect with a business in Manchester. It would have opened at the same time as Parkside, but building was delayed for a year due to shortage of funds and it eventually opened in 1872, one year after Parkside. The land for the building of both hospitals was purchased from the Governors of Macclesfield Free Grammar School, and some of the stonework was obtained from the same local Tegg's Nose and Windyway quarries. Mr John May, the influential Macclesfield solicitor, was involved with the building of both hospitals.

Parkside Hospital was funded by the County, and on completion had provision for 702 beds, whereas Macclesfield Infirmary was built as a result of a bequest from Joseph Tunnicliffe, a local silk mill owner, who left monies in endowment, the remainder being raised by public subscription. The Infirmary had provision for 116 beds, but on opening it had just 33 beds due to shortage of funds. One of the members of the selection panel who favoured James Stevens' plan for the Infirmary was the then incumbent of St Paul's Church, Macclesfield, the Reverend Henry Brient, himself a former architect, having designed the Berkshire Hospital at Reading.

Preparation of the Land for the New County Asylum Macclesfield

Having bought the land from the Governors of Macclesfield Free Grammar School for £10,562 15s, the preparation began on 25th March 1868, when Mr Henry Lovatt of Wolverhampton entered into a contract for the excavations and foundations. On 19th October of the same year a further contract was made for the construction of the superstructure, with the exception of the excited blocks and corridor ranges of single rooms connecting them to the other blocks. The cost for this came to £51,150. The Committee wished to postpone the completion of the excited blocks until a later date but the Commissioners in Lunacy wished them to complete the whole building at once; therefore a further contract was entered into on 24th August 1870 with Mr Lovatt for the additional works and completion of the whole building for the sum of £10,850.

The Foundations

The laying of the foundations began sometime during 1868. These were constructed of stone with adequate crawlways and heating ducts. By February 1869, despite lots of rain, most of the foundations had been laid. The nature of the ground proved to be somewhat unstable and some of the foundations had to be taken to a great depth. Extra piling was required for the clock tower foundations due to subsidence and many tons of concrete were used to provide greater stability. During the first year of building the water pipes were laid up to the site by the Macclesfield Water Works Company; the boreholes for the well being drilled later but then not found to be suitable for drinking water. The span of the bridge (now demolished) from Bridge Lodge was increased to comply with the requirements of the local authority. The bridge passed over Boughey Lane, later called Victoria Road. By the end of the first year the main drains were almost in situ.

Superstructure

Brick kilns were built and bricks made on site near to the current Springfield Road and Colville Road. A Pug mill was provided for mixing the clay to make the bricks. A mortar mix of 1 lime to 2 sand was used and they were laid in the style known as Flemish bond, as are most of the buildings at Parkside. The cottage near to the kilns was called Spring Cottage. A Mr Colville lived nearby and he objected to the nearness of the kilns to his property, writing several letters of complaint to Mr Griffiths. Eventually Mr Griffiths agreed to move the kilns a further 150 yards onto the hospital site. Some of the clay for making the bricks came from clay pits in the area of the Main Building. It seems that artisans working under what was Female 2 Ward very often came out covered in red brick dust, which did not occur elsewhere in the remaining areas of the building. Depths also seem to vary particularly under the old Male 5 Ward. Certainly the geological surveys of the site indicate the presence of a layer of clay. Brick making was delayed initially due to a damaged machine and the first batch of bricks were faulty. Following repairs to the machine there were no more problems. Women were also employed in the brickmaking team.

Further building progress took place during the next twelve months and during the winter months they worked by artificial light. By October 1869, the Hospital Church was ready for roofing and by 1870 most of the drains had been laid, along with the erection of a considerable amount of the superstructure. Negotiations commenced with the Borough Surveyor and the Macclesfield Board as to the best arrangements for sewage disposal and eventually the A.B.C. system was selected with the outflow from the treated sewage discharging into Whitfield Brook.

Correspondence took place with the Macclesfield Gas Company regarding a supply of gas for the asylum. Originally Mr Griffiths wanted to build a gasworks on site to supply the whole asylum, considering it more economical and cheaper in the long term. Eventually, following lengthy meetings with Mr Griffiths, the Macclesfield Gas Company and the Mayor of Macclesfield, it was decided that the Gas Company would supply a gas main from the gas works in Hibel Road to the asylum, but at a loss to the Company of several hundred pounds. Most of the building work was complete by May 1870 and Mr H Lovatt, the main contractor, was demanding payment. A meeting of Magistrates, Mr Griffiths and Mr Lovatt was held in the asylum grounds and it was agreed that Mr Griffiths pay Mr H Lovatt £10,850 for the completion of the works so far.

The building consists of red brick with white and blue brick dressings and parti-coloured brick arches. A portion of the high bank to the west of the female excited block beyond the laundry was removed to fill in the clay pits from which the clay was probably extracted to make the bricks. Stone enrichments were used for the clock tower and water towers. The main timbers are of Baltic fir and the joinery of Pitch pine, stained and varnished.

In the original plans the excited blocks at the extreme ends of the long corridor were to be built at a later date, but the Commissioners in Lunacy decided that they be built at the same time as the rest of the building. This was agreed to by Mr Griffiths and the workforce maintained the schedule, again working by artificial light during the winter months. By January 1871 most of the work was completed. The main roads round the building were set out by the best class of patients. The bridge was built over Boughey Lane to enable patients to get from one part of the grounds to the other without having to cross the road.

Over the three years that it took to build Parkside Asylum, Robert Griffiths spent much time actually on site supervising the building work. It must be remembered that he was also building the Herefordshire County Asylum at the same time, plus several other major works which must have necessitated much travelling between them.

Description of the Building

The following summary of the main building is taken from the Committee's report:

Female Side

Block No 1	92
In single rooms	21
	113
Block No 2	92
In single rooms	21
	113
Infirmary	68
Block No 3 excited class	57
	125
Total Females	351

Male Side

Block No 1	92
In single rooms	21
	113
Block No 2	92
In single rooms	21
	113
Infirmary	68
Block No 3 excited class	57
	125
Total Males	351
GRAND TOTAL	702

"The main building is about 912 feet in length and fronts Chester Road. In the centre on the south side stands the Superintendent's house connected with the main building by a covered verandah. The portion inhabited by the male patients consists of two blocks, with an infirmary and a block for the excited class, lying to the east of the Superintendent's house. The portion inhabited by the females is identical in plan with the male division, lying to the west.

On the north side of the building, occupying a corresponding position to the Superintendent's house, stands the clock tower, under which is the principal entrance to the asylum. Adjoining this are the administrative offices, with a large recreation and dining hall between them and the Superintendent's house. The women's infirmary lies between Blocks No 1 and 2 on the female side, and the men's infirmary between Blocks No 1 and 2 on the male side. The blocks set apart for the more excited class of patients are situated at the east and west extremities of the main building.

On the north side, to the west of the clock tower, are the wash houses and laundry. The brewery, engine houses, and workshops comprising tailors, shoemakers, carpenters, plumbers and other shops, occupy a position on the east side of the clock tower.

The various blocks are connected by spacious corridors, and each of the principal blocks is three storeys high. Each contains a day room with a south facing aspect, two small day rooms, dormitories, bathroom, lavatory, single rooms opening into the corridor, and other conveniences.

The infirmaries are two storeys high and each contains a day room, dormitories and bathrooms etc. The various rooms and passages throughout the building are well ventilated by means of single extraction flues, with cold air gratings in the external walls; the lantern windows in the building serve the double purpose of light and ventilation. Each side of the asylum has two airing courts, one for general use and the other for infirmary cases, each of which is divided from the rest of the grounds by a sunken wall. These airing courts are provided with verandahs so as to enable the patients to take their exercises in wet weather. There are three lodges in the grounds, the one on Chester Road being occupied by the Chief Attendant on the male side, and the two in Boughey Lane (Victoria Road) by the gardener and engineer. In the south west corner of the grounds stands the Church, apart from the rest of the buildings and capable of seating 430 persons. A roadway 16 feet wide runs from the principal entrance on Chester Road round the main building and from this a short carriage road 12 feet wide branches off to the Superintendent's house and the south side of the building, and a similar road runs from the lodge in Boughey Lane (Victoria Road) to join the principal road near the main door of the asylum".

The whole of the site on which the main building stands occupies about 9.5 acres. The large clock tower with its four clocks probably represents the most prominent feature of the building along with the two water towers, one on each side of the entrances to the grand hall (now burnt out). These three towers can be clearly identified from the hills to the east of Macclesfield on a clear day with a good pair of binoculars. The Superintendent's house was built on the higher ground to the south west so that good views of the south front and airing courts could be afforded. The basement consisted of storerooms, coal stores and heating chambers for the dining and recreation hall. The ground floor consisted of kitchen, servants' hall, cloakrooms, covered communication with six blocks of the pavilion, and the grand dining/recreation hall measuring 102 feet x 50 feet x 50 feet. Over the kitchen were the sleeping quarters for the servants. Dormitories, baths, lavatories and water closets made up the second floor for blocks 1, 2, 3 and 4. The four three storeyed blocks, two on either side of the grand hall, have flitched beams for the flooring joists. This is a method of joining large lengths of timber by bolting them together through a continuous central iron plate, cast iron boxes rather than tenon joints forming the junction between some beams.

The corridor range joining the blocks is 9 feet wide, with the original excited blocks forming the extreme ends. The dining and recreation hall was heated by hot water pipes, but originally other parts of the building were heated by ordinary coal fires. A vent flue was carried up in each chimney, and in the single rooms where there were no fireplaces a ventilating flue was formed over the ceiling. Single extractor flues were fed to cold air gratings in the external walls. These proved of great benefit during the war years, when strict blackouts meant the closing of all windows and painting them black, thus cutting down on ventilation. Some of the large county asylums did not have ventilation shafts and this caused considerable problems due to the build up of the products of combustion from the gas appliances and open fires.

The distance north to south from the clock tower through to the Medical Superintendent's house is about 240 feet in length. It is estimated that there are 1,000 windows, all of which were made to open, thus giving adequate light and ventilation. In the main hall lancet windows were fitted and the floor was originally pitch pine but later, following a fire, it was refloored with maple boards. Unfortunately a further fire gutted the main hall in 1988 and it is now burnt out. This floor was regarded as one of the best dance floors in the North of England and over the years some of the country's leading dance bands have played in the hall. The annual Fancy Dress Ball was also held in the main hall, started in the 1880s and regarded as one of the main social events of the year in the Macclesfield District, attracting interest from far and wide. To the south end of the grand hall was a stage, in front of which was a handsome proscenium for 16 players.

All day rooms were originally on the ground floor and connected with an estimated one mile of corridors. The heart of the building consisted of offices, Surgeon's and Matron's rooms, kitchens, dispensary, waiting rooms, store rooms and library. The Superintendent's house had a coach house and stable attached and in later years a conservatory was added at a cost of £120.

The building stones used in the ornamentation of the main building, church, bridge (part of which remains in Victoria Road) and the three lodges (one now demolished) were Hollington Stone brought from quarries near Uttoxeter, Yorkshire Stone and more locally Tegg's Nose Stone. Welsh slate was used for most of the roof in the form of Bangor Duchess Slating. A small quantity of Westmorland slate was also used.

The Clock Tower

The clock tower consists of five stages and stands forward of the main administrative block, facing north, providing the principal entrance to the main building. The height of the clock tower is 90 feet with most of the staging being 12 feet wide, apart from the final clock stage which is 14 feet wide.

Access to the inside of the tower is gained via a Slingsby roof exit sliding ladder from the first floor. The ladder ascends to a trap door in the ceiling corner. A weighted pulley cord is attached to the back of the door, allowing the door to remain open in any position. From here each stage is gained by a wide plain wooden staircase with rail to each platform. The clock mechanism is housed in a cabinet like structure with glass doors in front to prevent dust entering the mechanism; it is situated in the topmost stage of the tower. The two bells are housed below the clock mechanism at the top of the tall bay. On the south facing aspect of the tower spire a dormer window abuts out, having been used as a fire watch observation point during the Second World War. The four clock faces are of slate in two halves.

The clock mechanism is the original made by J.B.Joyce and Company Limited, Whitchurch. The date on the front of the clock mechanism is 1870 and the whole was purchased by Robert Griffiths, the designer and architect of the main building. Estimates indicate that Mr Griffiths had a choice of two clocks, one striking on the hour costing £179, the other striking on the quarters costing £214; no expense was spared so he chose the latter. Its dulcet chimes can still be heard today. At the front of the mechanism are three apertures into which the key is inserted to wind and alter the timing on the clock. A small platform is situated over the finger mechanism on the rear of each clock face. The large pendulum is accessible through a small door at the bottom of the housing case. Small lead weights sit on top of the pendulum. The central cogwheel mechanism from which four driving rods radiate to each clock face is encased in a neat box with apexed roof.

Despite the move towards modern day electric clocks, the Parkside Clock is wound up mechanically every Thursday morning. The firm who made the clock, J.B.Joyce, are the oldest established firm of tower clockmakers in the world. They were founded in 1690 and are noted for the manufacturing of the double three-legged gravity escapement in 1849, which was later used in the Great Clock of the Palace of Westminster, better known as 'Big Ben'. The company is still going strong today, and since 1945 has installed more than 2000 large public clocks in the British Isles, as well as cleaning, repairing and overhauling existing clocks.

The two bells were made by Mears and Standbank, Founders, London, and strike alternately every quarter hour, working via a pulley system attached to the clock mechanism. The metal pulley cords run in a wooden conduit partway down the third and fourth stages. A gas mantle remains fixed to a timber in the fourth stage, indicating an earlier form of lighting.

Additions

The farm buildings (now demolished) and chaplain's house (demolished 1994) were completed during 1871 after the Main Building had opened. After completion of the Main Building the Clerk of Works lived in Jeremiah Clarke's house and later the Chaplain, but conditions inside were very bad, so it was decided by Mr. Griffiths that extensive repairs would be too costly. The building was demolished, leaving the outbuildings intact. Mr. Griffiths then designed a new house for the Chaplain on the same site next to the original outbuildings and a separate water supply was provided from a well nearby. In 1904, after the Chaplain's post became non-resident, and at the same time that the nurses' home was built, the Chaplain's house became a private residence, then a Sisters' home. It was demolished in 1994, along with the original outbuildings which had been used to stable the horses of the visiting Magistrates on the days that they attended meetings in the committee room of the main building.

The whole of the cross shaped complex of the main building is Grade II listed, running from the original male excited block on the extreme end of the corridor range to the east to the original female excited block on the extreme end of the range to the west. Likewise from the clock tower facing north through to the former Medical Superintendent's house facing south. The laundry was also part of the original complex, near to the female excited block via a covered walkway. The two epileptic blocks facing north, latterly Female 6/7 and Male 7 were added later.

The south side of the main building has remained remarkably free of add on buildings, apart from two additions to the Medical Superintendent's house in the form of a small conservatory and in later years a wooden staff canteen. Two wooden occupational therapy huts, one of which served as a Chapel have been added on either side of the main hall. The walls across the airing courts of the two three-storeyed blocks on each side of the main hall have been demolished, and part of the verandah walkway leading from the Medical Superintendent's house to the male and female blocks have also gone to allow a roadway to pass through.

The north side of the building has had several additions over the years. The first was in 1891 when a female epileptic block was added between the clock tower and laundry. The second was the male epileptic block, which opened in the spring of 1903, between the clock tower and artisans yard. Both of these are in keeping with the rest of the building.

Another building already on site when the hospital was built was Bollington Barn House. This is situated on Victoria Road north of the Clock Tower at the top of the track leading down to the East Cheshire Hospice. In the early 1870s it was set aside for private patients, following this it became the residence of the Clerk of the Asylum. Later it was to become an Isolation Hospital for a short while then a residence for the Pathologist, and a further Doctor, and more latterly was used as a drug addiction unit during the 1970s. Eventually it was sold off and is still standing as a private residence.

The remaining add-on buildings have tended to mar the appearance of the north side; these include several small additions to the original laundry block which is now difficult to discern, a small fire station at the side of the main administration block, a generator shed, and wooden occupational therapy hut used for various purposes over the years.

To the east of the clock tower a wooden Works Department has been added. and numerous alterations have taken place around the boilerhouse area in front of the original artisans' yard and brewery.

Contractors

The main contractor for the building was Mr Henry Lovatt of Wolverhampton, and Messrs Coupe of Wigan supplied the engineering works. Mr Mellard of Rugeley supplied the water apparatus, and Messrs Finch the baths and lavatories. The pumping engine was supplied by Messrs Mellor and Son of Rainow, and the sewage engine by Messrs Coupe and Company. Cooking apparatus was supplied by Messrs Benham and Sons of Wigmore Street, London. The other sub-contractors were Mr Mellor of Macclesfield for the plastering and Mr Westwood of Dudley for the slating. Gas lighting was supplied from the Macclesfield Corporation Gas Works, and the fittings supplied by Messrs Messenger and Company of Birmingham.

Contractors for the furnishings were Messrs Blyth and Son for the general furniture, and Mr Adams of Fifeshire for the birch furniture. Messrs Cooper and Holt of Bunhill Row, London supplied the carpets. Messrs Merryweather and Sons provided a hand engine and hose in each block in case of fire. The Clerk of Works was Mr J Laidlaw.

By December 1871, the cost of the building stood at £125,893 10s 9d. the sum of £11,823 3s 5d being paid for out of the County Rate and £114,070 7s 2d had been borrowed, thus leaving £4,070 7s 2d due to the County Treasurer. It was estimated that a further sum of £15,929 12s 10d would be required for the eventual completion of the Asylum. Extra expenses had been incurred due to the difficulties with the foundations under the clock tower and parts of the four 3-storey blocks. Additional drainage due to the running sand and the fencing in of nearly three sides of the site as an additional provision to the original agreement all served to put up the cost. The tendency to erect high fences and walls around Asylums was very often born out of public pressure and fear rather than a need for them on the part of the patients.

Further expense was necessary when the Macclesfield Local Board refused to allow the Committee to pipe sewage outfall from the Asylum down Boughey Lane and connect it to the outfall from the Workhouse on Prestbury Road as originally agreed. They considered this would cause too much pollution into the River Bollin, so the Committee had to build their own sewage filters and beds. Additional land was also purchased from the Grammar School Governors at a cost of £2,885 19s 3d including tithes and two cottages plus land from a private owner on Chester Road for £350.

In order to meet the above costs a further sum of £20,000 was borrowed. The total cost of the building up to the completion of the original design came to £133,835 but with the additional costs incurred the final sum eventually stood at £141,823 3s 5d. On opening it was judged to be one of the best asylums in the Kingdom.

Opening Ceremony

The opening ceremony was announced in a London newspaper and the Asylum was opened for patients on 8th May 1871. The first group of patients were transferred from Upton Asylum in Chester and consisted of 99 females and 81 males, and by 30th October of that year 249 patients had been transferred. 31 males and 21 females were from the Macclesfield Union. Special arrangements were made with the Railway Company whereby through carriages were run from Chester to Macclesfield via Crewe and Harecastle (now Kidsgrove Station). Horse drawn carriages were provided from Upton Asylum to Chester Station, and likewise from Macclesfield Station to the Asylum. The whole operation was supervised and arranged by the Medical Superintendent, Dr Deas, with sufficient attendants providing escorts and no untoward incidents occurred.

During the period May to December 1871, 68 patients were admitted for the first time. Also during that same period, 22 were discharged, fourteen having recovered, one relieved, one not improved and six had died. At the end of the first year there were 295 patients. The records state that of these, five had become insane from disappointment in business, two through love affairs, two from fright, one over religion, fourteen from intemperance, two from old age, five from epilepsy, thirty six not ascertained, and various other causes. During the first five years of opening, contracts were signed with the joint counties of Abergavenny, Monmouth, Brecon and Radnor to take patients for four years. A number of patients were also admitted from Cumberland for a seven year period. A total of 134 people suffering from epilepsy were admitted over a four year period from 1871 to 1875 and throughout that time only one death occurred. In 1880 contracts were signed to accept patients from Salop Asylum and Birmingham Borough Lunatic Asylum at a charge of 14s per head per week. Many patients also came from workhouse lunatic wards and were transferred back to their original counties when new asylums had been built. Nearly half the total admissions between 1872 and 1880 were from districts other than Cheshire. By 1886 the average weekly maintenance costs for the mentally ill in the 52 English County Asylums was 8s 7d. At Parkside it was 8s 0d in 1886 and 7s 10d during 1887.

During the first year the staff consisted of the Medical Superintendent, Assistant Medical Officer, Chaplain, Clerk to the Visitors, Clerk of the Asylum, Storekeeper, Housekeeper, Head Male and Female Attendants, 20 Male and 37 Female Attendants, Servants, Shoemaker, Baker, Cowman, Engineer and Assistants, Farm Bailiff, Gardener and Hall Porter.

Visitors arriving at the Asylum clock tower would be received in the Hall Porter's room and from there would be shown to the relevent wards. The Medical Superintendent's room adjoined the central corridor leading from the main entrance door in the clock tower. Inside this room were two tell-tale clocks installed by Messrs Gent and Co of Leicester. These were wired to electric batteries in the respective corridors on the female and male blocks. Cards with figured times and numbers corresponding to the respective batteries in the wards revolved inside the clock cases. Each time the attendant passed the battery and touched it a hole was punched in the card. In the male wards there were always three attendants in regular circuit, and in the female wards, four in circuit. Some parts were visited every fifteen minutes, thirty minutes or two hours. In the epileptic wards attendants were present day and night. The tell-tale clock system was devised to ensure that the attendants were doing their job!

At that time the main hall was also used as a dining room, fitted out with rows of tables with clean table cloths provided twice weekly. The whole hall presented a lofty appearance, with its lancet windows providing plenty of light and its pitch pine floor and furniture giving stability. This was further enhanced by the judicious use of flowering and foliage plants and the busts of the two main political figures of the time, Lord Beaconsfield and Mr Gladstone, in brown, adorning either side of the proscenium.

Amusements for the patients consisted of a ball every week, theatre and concert evenings every now and then and a once a year picnic to Alderley Edge. When not employed in actual work the patients were allowed parole in the grounds or town.

The following extracts from an account of a visit to the Asylum by the local press in 1888, and later published in a book entitled '**A Walk Through the Public Institutions of Macclesfield**' by R Brown, gives a thorough insight into the conditions at that time:

"It is explained that till last year there was no such article of mechanical motion as a clock allowed. Perfect quiet as far as could be obtained was enjoined. In a happy moment the Committee of Visitors acceded to the suggestion of the Medical Superintendent that a clock might enliven what to most of the inmates could be a monotonous life; if this was so for the patients what must it have been like for the attendants. Since the fixture of the clocks there has been one unanimous verdict of approval from the unfortunates. To the females particularly the innovation came with particular welcome. Housewives, as a rule, are habituated to the presence of some sort of timepiece in their living-room when there are no children to "plague their lives". The ticking of the clock breaks the heavy monotony and daily routine. There was more melancholy truth in the remark of a patient than one would credit an insane person with, who when asked about the new addition to the already attractive room said "It looks more like home".

Our walk has occupied something like an hour and a half now and as the dinner bell has gone we are invited to see the patients at this important meal. In they come trooping from both sides of the building, and seat themselves at the tables, the males ranging themselves at those on the male side of the building and the females occupying seats next to their departments. Helpless cases and others who cannot be trusted amongst the rest of the patients have their meals in the wards, but as far as it can with safety be carried out, the principle of lively association at meal times is followed.

Seeing the patients at meal times, of course suggests the question - how do they live? We are informed that the first bell goes at 5.45 am, when all day attendants and nurses must be out of bed, at 6 o'clock the patients are got up in summer, and 7 o'clock in late autumn, winter and early spring. Those who can work are taken out to the farm or any outdoor occupation to which they have been put; the women to their sewing and knitting, and such as are sensibly-insane to cleaning up and house duties till eight o'clock when breakfast is served. Dinner varies with the day. Sunday roast beef, vegetables and bread; Monday soup and currant dumpling; Tuesday potato pie; Wednesday mutton or pork; Thursday Irish Stew of meat, potatoes, onions and liquor in which the previous day's meat was boiled; Friday fish and vegetables; Saturday Meat and potato pie of meat, potatoes, flour, onions and crust made with dripping.

Returning to their respective duties or pleasures, the supper bell recalls them at 6 o'clock, when each has a pint of tea and bread and butter, with sweet cake on Sundays. Then all are free from task and duty till 8pm, when to bed they go - a process which occupies, of the periods into which the day is divided, longer time than clothing them in the morning. A cursory visit to the kitchen is not the least pleasant item in the course of our stroll . One of Benhams of London apparatus for roasting by gas and boiling by steam is in use, and the cook giving it the highest possible character for efficiency, cleanliness and rapidity of heating. The attire of the scullery maids bears testimony to the fact that everything under the cook's superintendence goes on with that clock-work care and discipline which conduces at once to cleanliness and comfort. Coming once more to the waiting room, an opportunity is afforded to talk over what we have seen.

The treatment of the patients naturally forms one of the first topics discussed. We are all agreed as to the importance of regular and frequent outdoor exercise afforded the patients in the airing yards and walks within the grounds. Parties we are told are, when the weather permits, sent out regularly to walk in the roads and lanes around the Asylum and suitable occupation is provided as far as possible for all who are able or can be induced to occupy themselves. The farm, the kitchen garden and at one time laying out the grounds, afforded abundantly healthy occupation for a number of the men; others assist in the wash-house, the kitchen, the store, and the wards. The women are employed in the laundry, the kitchen, domestic offices, and needlework. From the records it appears that more than two-thirds of the residential number are so employed. Means of mental occupation are also provided. A library has been formed embracing works in all branches of general literature, the shelves containing numerous volumes. On the tables in the day rooms of the wards are daily and weekly newspapers with occasional magazines and a profusion of illustrated periodicals purchased at less than half-cost from the Free Library and other institutions in the borough.

On Sundays there are religious services in the Church and on weekdays every sort of rational amusement a sane person enjoys or engages in to relieve the monotony and pressure of their care and lighten and enliven the daily demands of business, and the necessities of life. Every possible variety of decoration pervades the entire building in keeping with the character of the room in which the patients are classified.

Nurses and attendants are clad in the ordinary attire of everyday life, and the inmates themselves never wear, in but few cases, and that where no private apparel is available, anything approaching a uniform dress. The men wear cloth, moleskin, corduroy; the women have gowns, also made up of various materials, cotton, linsey, and wool. Plaid shawls are in common use with the females and some of the dirty cases have strong, but neat linen jackets which obviate the necessity for a removal of the upper part of their outer dress when skirts only require to be changed for cleanliness sake.

Of escapes there are few. Medical authorities, we are told, look upon the attempt to resume associations and duties of the outer world as a sign of returning sanity. Insane people have no sense of responsibility; as soon as the idea of personality begins to dawn the active spirit longs for its usual haunts. There are many instances in the records in support of this theory. Early in the history of this Asylum a patient - an old man and rather a character in his way - who usually had a good deal of liberty, took a restless turn every few months. Off he went one day to revisit the scenes of his former labours as an ostler at a town some miles distant. There was no anxiety about him as he had previously slipped out of keeping, and had returned of his own accord. On the first occasion, the second day after he left, he went to the police office and ordered the police to take him back to the asylum as he was "too tired to walk."

World-wide Developments

It is interesting to identify some of the key developments taking place in the world during the early years of Parkside. Mr William Ewart Gladstone (1809-1898) was the Liberal Prime Minister and Queen Victoria was in the 34th year of her reign; she became Empress of India in 1876. The novelist Charles Dickens, writer of Oliver Twist, Nicholas Nickleby and David Copperfield, died in 1870 and in 1873 the composer of some of the world's greatest piano concertos, Sergei Vassilyevich Rachmaninov, was born.

The Franco-Prussian War was fought between 1870 and 1871. The Prussians were the victors and this ultimately led to the formation of the German Empire consisting of 38 kingdoms and states united into one country. In 1800 there was no such country as Italy but gradually Venetians, Romans or Neopolitans started to see themselves as Italians and after many bitter struggles Italy finally became a united country in 1871. The Zanzibar slave market also closed in 1871 as a result of British intervention; meanwhile America was still struggling with the aftermath of its Civil War which had ended six years previously. The First Boer War had yet to start in 1881 and in the same year Tzar Alexander II of Russia was assassinated by a Polish student on 13th March.

By 1869 the Suez Canal had been built by France and Egypt and later, in 1875, Britain bought the Egyptian share of the Canal. The Canal was a major boost to British trade, cutting the journey to India by 4000 miles. Meanwhile the canal system in Great Britain was facing competition from the railways, which eventually led to its decline. The electric telegraph was sending the result of the 1871 English Derby to India five minutes after the race, and by 1874 the typewriter had arrived, to be followed by the telephone in 1876 and Edison's cylinder phonograph in 1877.

In Great Britain, the Health Acts of 1872 and 1875 compelled local authorities to appoint Health Officers and improve water supplies and sanitary conditions. The first board schools were set up for poor children, paid for out of public money in 1870 and education was made compulsory up to the age of 11 in 1881. Ten years later in 1891, it became free, and grant-aided Grammar Schools were to be introduced in 1902. Meanwhile, in Macclesfield, towards the end of the century a School of Art had been established along with a Technical School, Free Library and Infirmary. The first motor vehicle, a commercial van, to pass through the streets of Macclesfield did so three weeks prior to the Diamond Jubilee Celebrations of Queen Victoria in June 1897.

The Epileptic Wards

The first major addition to the main building was a two-storeyed female epileptic block, opening in 1891, built to accommodate 96 patients. It is situated between the clock tower and laundry facing north. Previous to this, 82 people suffering from epilepsy were cared for in a ward in the main building. The contractor for the building was Mr Gladwell, and the total cost for construction amounted to £6,756 9s 9d. Heating was provided by a slow combustion stove and the furniture was supplied by Arighi Bianchi of Macclesfield. The bottom storey was for female epileptics and the top storey for general cases. Accommodation was provided for ten nursing staff. The cost per bed was about £133 including furniture and the price of extra land, purchased in 1892 at a cost of £4,298 and consisting of 16 acres 2 roods and 17 poles. This had been necessitated because of the growing numbers in the hospital. Of the £133, forty five pounds represented the cost of the land and £15 the cost of furnishing, clothing and bedding, thus reducing the cost of the building to £73 per bed. The building was constructed to the designs of Mr Stanhope Bull, who was the County Surveyor for Cheshire. It is more or less in keeping with the original Main building by Griffiths, apart from some archwork which is somewhat elaborate. On completion the total accommodation rose to 744.

The second major addition to the main building was the male epileptic ward, situated between the clock tower and artisans' yard facing north. It was designed and planned by the County Architect, Mr Harry Beswick, and the then Medical Superintendent, Dr T.S.Sheldon, providing accommodation for 50 male patients at a cost of £6,782 including furniture. It opened in the spring of 1903 and is architecturally in keeping with the main building, but of slightly different design and ornamentation than the female epileptic ward. In later years both the female and male epileptic wards were used for elderly care wards or sick wards.

The Nurses' Home, next to the Church, was also built at about the same time in 1902 for female nurses. Up to this time, for a period of 30 years following the opening of the hospital in 1871, the nursing staff slept in rooms adjacent to or above the wards in the main building. With the completion of the Nurses' Home these rooms were then vacated and used for patients.

Further Plans

In a report to the Asylum Extension Committee in 1892, Dr T.S.Sheldon recommended the building of Annexes both at Parkside and at Upton in Chester. On 26th September 1893, the land for the proposed Infirmary/Admission Hospital, later known as the Annexe, towards the east of the main building was purchased from the Governors of Macclesfield Free Grammar School. The plans for the Parkside Isolation or Fever Hospital were also drawn up and the contract awarded to Lambert and Son, Builders, Altrincham. The Isolation Hospital opened in 1896 and was used for fever cases for many years. It was designed by Mr Stanhope Bull and cost £3,277.

It was during the year of Queen Victoria's Diamond Jubilee in 1898 that many of the main sewers were laid by George Roylance, Waters Green, Macclesfield, from the main hospital building to the Macclesfield Corporation sewers on Chester Road and Victoria Road. Permission was also given to lay soil pipes to the detached buildings, i.e. Farm Bailiff's House, Slaughter House, Victoria Road Lodge and two cottages in Victoria Road. The Chaplain's House and the Lodge at the main entrance on Chester Road were also connected to the main sewer on Chester Road. Up to that time a system of sewage disposal called the ABC system was used, and this apparently is similar to modern day systems. The sewage was piped to two tanks and a filter bed near the main entrance on Victoria Road. After filtration and purification the water drained into Whitfield Brook, which flows through Macclesfield Cemetery and ultimately into the River Bollin. The regulations for this stated that the water must be kept unpolluted as it flows through the cemetery. The manure obtained following treatment was sold by the hospital for 70 shillings per ton.

In 1902 further land was purchased from Macclesfield Grammar School on the north side of Victoria Road to provide a quantity of farmland for further cultivation for the forthcoming extensions of the Annexe Hospital. The total land bought amounted to 17 acres 1 rood and $8\frac{1}{2}$ perches.

Water Supply

On the 24th January 1873 a contract was entered into with Mather & Platt, of Manchester, to sink a well to a depth of 30 feet, lined with cast iron cylinders. A borehole was to be drilled from the well into the red sandstone to the required depth and tubed. Pumping apparatus, steam and labourers were to be supplied by the committee.

This was later carried out with the total bore depth being 344 feet. Solid rock was reached at 227 feet and the tubes discontinued at a depth of 292 feet, 100 tons of pressure being required to force the tubes down. On operation water rose to 179 feet of the surface and from there was pumped to the storage tanks in the water towers on either side of the main hall. In later years the well was enlarged and brick-lined part way down. The water from the well was found to be unsuitable for drinking purposes, so a supply was piped from Macclesfield Waterworks to the main building near the well. The well water was used for the hot water heating system, fire hydrant system, and in later years to provide water for the Annexe water tower.

The first analysis of the water from the well was done in 1874 but the hardness was unsatisfactory and it was thought that water other than from the new red sandstone was finding its way into the borehole. On the 11th November 1877, Dr J.Campbell Brown from Liverpool analysed the water and discovered the total hardness to be double the original analysis. He suggested a filter be installed to prevent sand entering the water and a separate tank be used for rainwater, which at that time was collected from the roof of the main building. The civil engineer engaged to improve the well, Mr Arthur C.Groats, for G.H.Hill Esq, Albert Square, Manchester, recommended $9\frac{1}{2}$ inch holes, a water yield to be equal to 100 gallons per minute, pump size $1\frac{1}{2}$ inches, and the power of the pump to be sufficient to raise 150 gallons per minute 300 feet high. On 23rd June 1886 work began on the construction of a storage reservoir on ground adjacent to the well north of the artisans yard. The dimension of the tank was 60 feet x 150 feet x 6 feet, with a holding capacity of 248,000 gallons. This was surrounded by a 7 feet high fence.

On 9th November 1893, an agreement was entered into with the Macclesfield Corporation to lay a 12 inch main from Macclesfield Market Place to the junction of Cumberland Street and Jordangate; then via a 9 inch main along Cumberland Street onto Prestbury Road. From there it would continue along Victoria Road to the Asylum Lodge and onto the Asylum water tanks. The Committee agreed to pay 30% of the cost towards the new main and a fixed charge of 6d per 1,000 gallons, with a five yearly revision. Later, in 1923, the charges were increased by the Macclesfield Corporation to $7\frac{1}{2}$d per 1,000 gallons, despite much opposition by the Committee, and in 1933 the charges were brought into line with those generally charged for trade purposes. Again, the Committee were not happy about this and referred the matter to the Ministry of Health, but eventually they agreed to pay the charges.

In April 1899, an improved air lift pumping plant was installed, lifting 6,000 gallons per hour from 200 feet below the surface into one of the storage tanks. In 1904 the upper portions of the main building water towers became unsound and were completely rebuilt.

Over a twelve month period from 1906 to 1907 problems arose with the air lift pump and it broke down thirteen times, so further improvements were recommended. Colonel Antrobus and Mr Ball, representing the Committee, together with the Asylum Engineer, visited several places to see other types of air lift pumps, and subsequently a new pump was installed by Isler and Company, Artesian Works, Bear Lane, Southwark, London. A general servicing and upgrading of the well was carried out along with further deepening of the borehole to a depth of 344 feet. The total cost for these improvements amounted to £505 10s.

In 1910, a water softening plant was installed, because of the rapid choking up of the hot water pipes and boilers, and problems were again encountered with the air compressor. On 25th April 1911, £370 was provided for a new compressor and a 7½ inch high pressure steam cylinder to improve the economy of the plant. Further improvements to the supply took place in 1916, when a hot water pump was installed in the main building to remedy a deficit in heating, and an extension of the settling tank for the water softening plant was carried out at a cost of £100, along with additional softener, with much improvement in the purity of the water. At the same time another important milestone was reached with the supply of another essential service, namely electricity, when the whole of the main building was finally lit with electric lighting. The wiring of the building had started in the 1890s; prior to that gas lighting was used.

In 1919 a scheme was adopted by the Committee for collecting more rainwater from the roof of the main building to be used for boiler feed purposes. Two sewage tanks near the North East Lodge, which had not been used since 1894, were treated with puddled cement and rendered capable of holding 60,000 gallons of rainwater from the Asylum roof. This effected a saving of £60-£70 per annum in water charges by storing rainwater and piping it to the main boilers. The Manchester Steam Users Association heard about this and commented favourably upon the technique.

During 1931, an additional settling tank was completed for water softening purposes for water from the hospital well. By this time, of course, the hospital had expanded considerably and this tank held a further 170,000 gallons. In 1933 breakdowns of the air compressor pump started to recur, thus necessitating extra supplies from the Macclesfield Corporation at a much higher cost than from the hospital's own well, so an additional air compressor was purchased from Messrs Bellis and Morcom Limited.

Following the purchase of Upton Priory Estate in 1940, the water main was extended. In 1942 it was felt necessary to increase the total water storage capacity due to the expansion of the hospital and to build up reserves in case of fire damage to the buildings during the war years. Extra reserves were added by the construction of water storage tanks in various parts of the hospital grounds and parkland, amounting to a further 750,000 gallons. The main source of supply continued to be from the hospital well, the water being pumped to the various underground storage tanks, and the main drinking water supply was from two mains from Macclesfield Borough Council Waterworks. As water technology advanced, further additions, modifications and improvements took place, but the main sources remain up to the present day, with of course a much reduced capacity due to the gradual rundown of the hospital. The overall storage capacity, including rainwater, at one time amounted to 1,248,000 gallons, the bulk of this supplied from the hospital's own supply; a credible performance in self-sufficiency and, combined with the capacity in the three water towers, equal to the storage capacity of the old Buxton Road storage reservoir in Macclesfield.

The Church

The Hospital Church of St Luke, is situated to the south west of the main building and was built at the same time to designs by Robert Griffiths in 1868-71. The style is Early English Gothic, with nave, transepts, chancel, organ chamber and vestry. It has a fine open timbered roof and the chancel and aisles are fitted with Minton encaustic tiles. The organ is the original and rated by some as the best in Macclesfield, along with the beautiful acoustic qualities of the interior of the building. The stonework is in coarsed rubble with dressed limestone, and is buttressed diagonally at its west end. There is a nave of five bays, and the whole interior has some fine stonework of a very high standard. The original plan for the church included either a tower or spire but this was abandoned on grounds of cost. This may account for the rather long nave built to seat 430 and not 700 as incorrectly stated when the building was listed as Grade II in 1989.

In Victorian times the sexes were segregated and separate entrances were provided into the church, with the woman's entrance on the north side, and the men's entrance on the south side. The attendants occupied the first three rows of pews, and the Medical Superintendent sat behind the choir. The back three rows were for people suffering from epilepsy, and consisted of specially adapted pews in case they had a fit. A bell-cote with two bells is situated on the west end of the roof. At the end of the first year of building, the Church was ready for roofing and by July of 1871, Sir H Mainwaring was arranging for the consecration of the Church by the Bishop.

The Chaplain's residence was originally on site and the first Chaplain, the Reverend J.A.Ladbrooke, BA, lived in the house formerly occupied by Mr Jeremiah Clarke. For the first 33 years the Chaplain's post was a resident one, but in 1904 it became non-resident, following the appointment of the Reverend Lucius F.N.B.Smith, MA. Each year from 1871 until 1947 the Chaplain submitted an annual report to the Committee. After 1947 separate reports were done by each denomination.

In late Victorian times the influence of the Church was much greater than it is today and religious life played a much larger part in the daily lives of people, extending to other facets of development such as education, bodily well-being and politics. The Chaplain's role at Parkside was an important one and he was responsible not only for the spiritual and moral well-being of the patients and staff but also in part for their education and physical fitness. The library was the responsibility of the Chaplain and he had to keep it well stocked with books and periodicals. The books were often purchased as seconds from the Macclesfield Free Library on Park Green; others were donated to the hospital by the local gentry and other private bodies and individuals. Most wards were supplied with newspapers and illustrated weeklies.

Regular evening classes were held in the church, conducted by the Chaplain. Subjects included not only religious matters but politics and literary classes. Confirmation classes, both for staff and patients, were held regularly. A hospital choir was in existence and for many years a regular service was held in the main hall for staff and patients. A large number of staff played musical instruments and accompanied the patients in their singing. Communion for staff was held at 6 30am and was usually well attended from when the Church was opened in 1871 until the 1940s. Each day the Chaplain would visit all the wards in the hospital, giving support, help and advice, as well as carrying out the daily services. The Chaplain's duties also included gym instruction classes and the training of male patients and staff in the recreation department, including billiards, games and music. Music was always well represented, with regular concerts given either in the bandstand near the original Medical Superintendent's house or in the main hall and, following completion of the Annexe, in the Annexe Hall. A staff orchestra was in existence for three quarters of the hospital's history, and probably started when Dr T.S.Sheldon appointed Thomas Hughes as Musician Attendant in the summer of 1896.

With the gradual decline of the horse drawn carriage and the growing use of motorised carriages towards the end of the nineteenth century, the hospital choir were taken on many trips to surrounding beauty spots, concerts and other functions, along with the regular patients' trips. The provision of a 14-seater charabanc in 1923 added greatly to this.

During 1893, the Church was struck by lightning, occasioning a claim on the insurance for £12 14s, followed by the fixing of two lightning conductors at a cost of £28. In those days lightning conductors were tested every six months.

Services for Roman Catholics began in 1903 conducted by the Reverend Father Carton from the Church of St Alban, Chester Road. When it was decided to make the Chaplain's post non-resident in 1904, the Commissioners in Lunacy had to give their approval and following this the Chaplain's house, which by that time was on Chester Road, was let as a private residence and an Assistant Curate was appointed. At Harvest Festival times, gifts of fruit and flowers were received from surrounding country halls. In 1912 it was the turn of W.W.Brocklehurst Esq, who kindly donated huge amounts of fruit and flowers from the gardens of nearby Henbury Park. In 1906, the Reverend Lucius Smith resigned to take up a new post as Archdeacon and Canon of Ripon, later becoming Suffragan Bishop of Knaresborough. During 1907 the Reverend Darwin Wilmott, Headmaster of Macclesfield Grammar School conducted 51 services in the Church due to the Reverend Rhodes' failing health. Eventually in 1908 the Reverend Rhodes resigned due to ill health, the Reverend H.Norman Lowndes being appointed from St Paul's Church in Macclesfield. At this time weekly services were started for non-conformists.

During the Great War years, Church services had to be held in Uplands dining hall and the larger day rooms in the Annexe due to a shortage of coal to heat the boilers and the recurring influenza epidemics. It is also worthy of note that men attended the services in greater numbers during the war years.

In 1936 the Chaplain attended a conference on spiritual healing. At that time scientific and medical research was gaining greater momentum, with many new discoveries and treatments starting to take place. On his return from the conference, the Chaplain cited in his report the dilemma at that time between science and religion:

"God answers prayers by giving us something to do for ourselves. We believe the chief answers to prayers for healing are to be found in diligent medical research and careful application of medical science. We are hampered by some who put prayer before medical science. We believe Pastor and patient may

cooperate with medical science."

In 1941 the Reverend Canon T.J.Nash, MA, Vicar of Birtles, Chaplain of Parkside, was conferred with the degree of Honourary Canon of Chester Cathedral.

A brass plaque inside the Church is dedicated to the memory of the Reverend Thomas Woodrow Dix, MA(Oxon), who was appointed Chaplain in 1877 and died on 25th April 1900, after 23 years service. Following the death of the Reverend Dix, the Reverend George Brocklehurst was appointed on 1st October 1900. There were 78 applicants for the post, with a salary of £200 per annum. Another plaque is in memory of John Barker, a much loved and respected patient of the hospital, who worshipped at the Church for 50 years from 1932 until 1982. One of the Church's longest serving and most loyal members was Mr C.W.L.Hawkins, who was the organist for 52 years. He died on 9th July 1943. The next organist to be appointed was Mr Edgar Gulliford, who held the post from 1944 to 1978; a small plaque inside the Church is dedicated to his memory. Another small plaque is in memory of Mrs Patricia Parkyn of North Rode, Bosley, Macclesfield, who donated the electric lighting for the Church in the early 1900s.

In Macclesfield Cemetery can be found a memorial to Catherine Kelly who died on her way to Church. The inscription reads as follows.

Of your charity pray for the soul of Catherine Kelly
who died May 30th 1880 aged 44 years.
She was for 18 years a nurse in the Asylums of the County.
This stone was erected by the staff of Parkside Asylum.
In the midst of life we are in death.

Catherine Kelly originally worked at Upton Asylum, Chester, which of course was the original Cheshire County Asylum. She was transferred to Parkside Asylum on its completion in May 1871. Described as a hard working, loyal and considerate nurse she typified the large number of nurses who have worked at Parkside on the wards in the front line of treatment. Such people can only be described as 'the salt of the earth' and have been the mainstay of the hospital throughout its 125 year history.

The Church saw many years of devoted service by a variety of Chaplains, patients, nurses and artisans. At Harvest Festivals and Christmas time the Church was often packed to overflowing with extra chairs brought in to accommodate the huge number of people attending. Many of the Chaplains went on to assume posts of greater responsibility in the Church Ministry at other churches and cathedrals. Sadly, the last service was held in the Church in January 1994 and its future is yet to be decided.

Twenty months later saw the closure of the original 1871 building. The last group of patients were transferred from the Main Building to the Annexe on 22nd September 1995. The following week and with almost indecent haste a fleet of removal vans arrived to transfer the remaining administration departments to the Annexe. By Thursday 26th September, the Main Building was all but closed. The clock on the slender tower kept going but eventually wound itself down towards the end of the following week, the fingers on the four faces stopped at 7.30pm and the chimes ceased. The notable public clock had been wound every week and kept ticking for a century and a quarter, spanning five generations. Its final stoppage* truly marked the end of an era in the treatment of the mental illness in Macclesfield and the County.

*Since restarted

Main stores c1920

Dr Cormac's swimming pool under construction,
east of the Medical Superintendent's House.
L to R are Jack Jones (joiner), Jack Scragg
(Foreman plumber) and Alfred Jones (joiner and
brother of Jack).
Jack Scragg also contructed and glazed the fire
watch dormer window on the roof of the clock
tower.

Circular windows in the corridors linking the Administration Block with the main central corridor. The water towers with leaded ogee roofs can be seen in the background.

The bridge on Victoria Road, now demolished.

The Main Entrance from Victoria Road.

Medical Superintendent's House c1900 (Still standing, 1996)

The Clock Tower

A fine overall view of the four 3-storied blocks c1900.
The excited block airing court can be seen to the left.

The 1870 clock mechanism of J B Joyce of Whitchurch,

Original wrought iron work at the top of the stairs in the main administration block.

Positioning of profiles for two large underground water storage tanks of 200,000 gallon
capacity. The workmen are standing in the bottom of the tank, and include
Fred Moss, Bill Richardson and George Nixon, circa 1929.

Attendants on Male 3 corridor, Main Building, c1925

David Clarkson and Ted Proctor at work in the bakehouse c1940.

Austin convertable ambulance/sitting car, parked outside the Medical
Superintendent's House c1948.

Inside the Main Hall, originally used for dining purposes.

The Main Hall following the disastrous fire in August 1988.

Nurses' Home, built 1902

The original Chaplain's House of 1872, designed by Robert Griffiths. In 1904, it was used as a Nursing Sister's home. This picture shows it in a terrrible state of dilapidation, prior to demolition in 1994.

The church of St Luke, opened in 1871 and still standing (1995)

Interior of the church, 1995.

In Memory of
Thomas Woodrow Dix M.A.Oxon.
CLERK IN HOLY ORDERS, CHAPLAIN TO THIS INSTITUTION,
Who Died April 25th 1900,
After 23 years' service.
THIS TABLET
IS PLACED HERE BY HIS COLLEAGUES & FRIENDS.

Plaque in memory of
Reverend Thomas Woodrow Dix
MA (Oxon)

Bridge Lodge
The remains of the bridge can be
seen in the foreground, right.
(1996)

Price list of various
mouldings for the Main
Building prepared by Robert
Griffiths circa 1867

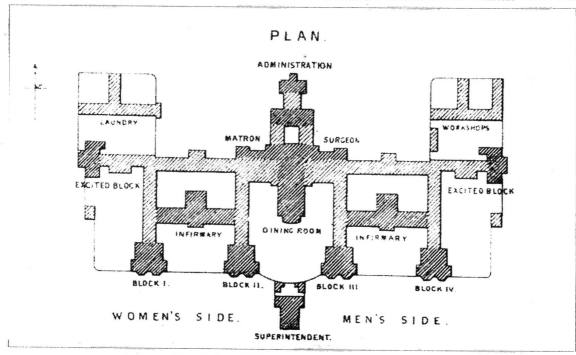

Layout of the Main Building from the 'Building News' of 1871

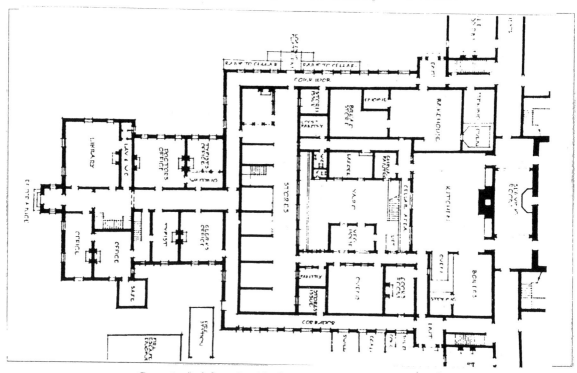

Central administration block, stores and kitchen areas 1940

The Main Building shortly after completion in 1871. Note the spoil heaps.

South side of the Main Building some years later, following landscaping.

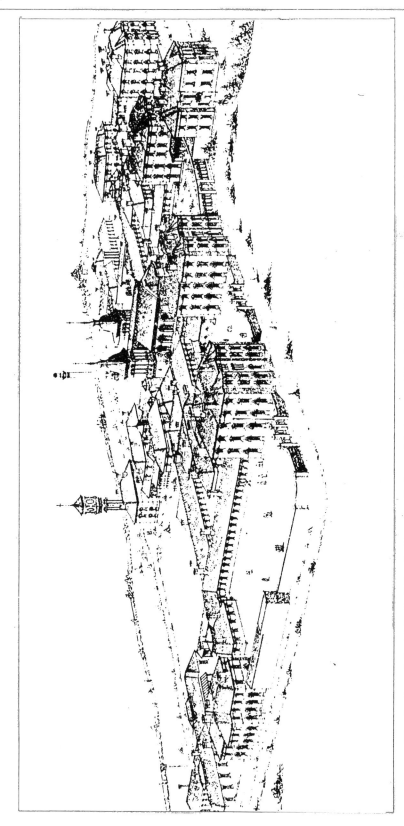

Sketch plan of the Main Building built to the designs of Robert Griffiths in 1868-71. Taken from the "Building News" of 1871

CHAPTER 4
The Annexe, East Villa, West Villa and Uplands

Towards the end of the nineteenth century the admission rates began to rise at Parkside as at many other institutions, brought about in part by segregation and classification in the workhouses and a growing need to try and understand the nature of mental illness, handicap and epilepsy. Treating sufferers in separate institutions away from the workhouses had started to reduce poor conditions and overcrowding. There was also a big rise in the admission of people suffering from infectious diseases, particularly tuberculosis, plus the elderly and infirm. It was felt that an Infirmary and reception area was needed at Parkside so that proper classification could take place. Accordingly, in the mid-1890s, it was decided to build a detached Infirmary/Admission Hospital to the east of the Main Building.

The design and planning for the new building was undertaken in 1899 by the County Architect for Cheshire, Mr. Harry Beswick, although some of the early drawings had been done by his predecessor, Mr Stanhope Bull, just before his death in 1895. The Medical Superintendent, Dr T.S.Sheldon and the clerk of works at Parkside, Mr William Longson were also heavily involved during the planning stage.

Harry Beswick was a native of Chester and was educated at the Kings School, where he was awarded the Westminster Gold Medal. He was articled to T.M.Lockwood, who in turn was a contemporary of John Douglas, both being famous Chester architects of the late Victorian era. The influence of both Douglas and Lockwood on Beswick was reflected in some of his brick buildings. Another famous architect of that era, Ormrod Maxwell Ayrton 1874-1960, was articled to Beswick in 1891, later becoming assistant to W.A.Pite in 1897 and Edward Lutyens from 1897 to 1900. Following Beswick's appointment to the post of architect to the Cheshire County Council in 1895, a position which he held for 30 years, he began to design many beautiful buildings throughout Cheshire, particularly schools and other public buildings. Some of the buildings he designed are listed and he was responsible for the report and discovery of a Roman building in Northgate Street Chester. The earliest parts of Shoemakers Row, Northgate Street, Chester, Nos.21-23 (1897) and No.3 (1898-9) were built to the designs of Harry Beswick. His most notable schools included the Grammar School, Ruskin Road, Crewe in 1909, done in Free Neo-Georgian style with 23 bay facade of red brick and red terracotta; the Grammar School, Marlborough Road, Bowden in 1911, with red brick and orange terracotta; and more locally, the County High School for Girls, Fence Avenue, Macclesfield, built between 1908-09 in the Neo-Georgian style with cupola. This is now the girls division of the Kings School, Macclesfield. Private works included the rebuilding of Oakfield House; Chester Zoo in 1892, and a series of cottages at Port Sunlight village. For many years he had a private business in the Grosvenor Buildings Chester. This later became Henry Beswick & Son and then W.H.Beswick, Architects, Chester. During the 1920s he lived in Queens Park and he died on July 8th 1929, aged 73.

The Annexe was part of a series of extensions which took place at the start of the twentieth century and included the Male Epileptic Block and Female Nurses' Home. Mr Beswick designed all of these. The total cost for the Annexe, Male Epileptic Block and Nurses' Home came to £80,359 11s 11d. It was designed primarily as an Infirmary/Admission building for 206 patients, but when completed it was found it could accommodate 220 patients without interfering with the requisite air space necessary for an Infirmary. Some considered it a miniature asylum almost independent of the Main Building and compared it favourably with 10 other new asylums built between 1899-1905.

Name of Asylum	Opened	No of beds	Cost not including land or furniture	Cost per bed
Winwick (Lancashire) built as a chronic asylum	1902	2050	£431,635	£210
Lincoln County (Kesteven Division)	1902	420	£138,682	£330
Nottingham County	1902	420	£147,086	£325
Staffordshire (Cheddleton)	1899	618	£252,821	£409
Sussex (East)	1903	1115	£322,275	£336
Croydon (County Borough)	1903	462	£210,893	£456
West Ham (County Borough)	1901	800	£322,149	£402
Brecon and Radnor (County)	1903	364	£124,369	£341
Yorkshire (Scaletor Park)	1902	246	£89,037	£362
Middlesex NewAsylum	1905	1200	Total cost not given	£345
Cheshire - Parkside extensions				
Male Epileptic Ward	1903	270	£76,503	£284
Infirmary Annexe	1905			

(Taken from the Blue Book of the Commissioners in Lunacy, June 1905.)

The main contractors employed for the foundations and drainage system were Messrs Isaac Massey and Sons, of Alderley Edge, and the superstructure, including the new Dynamo House, was built by Messrs W.A.Peters and Sons of Rochdale. The Dynamo House was built separately away from the Annexe in the workshops block of the main building. Two direct coupled steam dynamos were provided to give 35 kilowatts on 220/225 volts, and one direct coupled at 15 kilowatts on 220 volts. The building was constructed of Darley Dale and Yorkshire stone. Heating and ventilation were provided by Messrs Ashwell and Nesbitt Ltd of Leicester, and the electric plant by Messrs J.H.Holmes and Company, Newcastle-on-Tyne. The wiring and fittings were by Messrs D.Firth and Sons of Manchester and Hyde. Cooking apparatus was supplied by Messrs Moorwood and Sons Company Ltd of Sheffield.

The principal contractors for the furniture were the well established local firm Arighi Bianchi and Company Ltd, Macclesfield, along with Mr W.R.Brown, Mr C.A.Day, Mr.H.C.Wright and Mr H.Challinor, all well known local businesses in Macclesfield. Messrs Waring and Gillow, Manchester, were the only non-local contractors for the furniture. Clothing and bedding were supplied by Messrs D Stewart and Company of London and Mr J.B.Walker, Macclesfield. The telephones, clocks and bells were supplied by Gent and Company of Leicester.

The Opening Ceremony

The Annexe was formally opened on 19th July 1905 by Colonel Dixon, the Chairman of the County Council, in the unavoidable absence through illness of Colonel Antrobus, the Chairman of the Parkside Committee, and in the presence of about 70 invited guests including the Vice-Chairman of the County Council, the Chairman of Upton Asylum Committee, the Mayor of Macclesfield, the Deputy Mayor of Stockport, and representatives of Birkenhead County Borough. The Chairmen or Vice-Chairmen of the following Unions were also present: Macclesfield, Stockport, Ashton, Bucklow, Congleton and Hayfield.

At a luncheon presided over by the Deputy Chairman of the Committee, Colonel Brocklehurst, a presentation was made to Colonel Antrobus of his portrait, in token of his long and devoted services as Chairman for a period of $22\frac{1}{2}$ years. The portrait was accepted by Mrs Antrobus on behalf of her husband and she expressed his wish that the Committee should keep the portrait and hang it up in the board room at the hospital.

The description of the Annexe following its opening in 1905 reads as follows:

"The entrance to the Annexe is on the north side, the approach being from Victoria Road, and adjoining the entrance are the following: Medical Officer's Consulting Room, Enquiry Office, Porters' Room, with Pathological Room and Library above. After passing these and turning to the right will be found the following rooms: Reception and Dressing Rooms, Bathroom and Mortuary for male patents, and also a room for male visitors, whilst turning left will be found similar rooms for female patients. Near the above on the male side are the Assistant Doctor's apartments, and on the female side similar apartments for the Matron.

In the centre is the administration block consisting of sculleries, store rooms and large dining hall, with Billiard and Mess Rooms for male attendants on one side and nurses' sitting room and Mess Rooms on the other. At the centre of the building rises the water tower to a height of 100 feet, containing two tanks each capable of holding 20,000 gallons, which is supplied from the Asylum artesian well.

On each side of the building there is a ventilating air shaft and tower. To the south of the Dining Hall is the Operating Theatre and Dispensary with a Photographic Studio and Dark Room, whilst on the extreme south of the building stands the residence built for the Assistant Medical Officer who is in medical charge of the Annexe.

The building is lighted by electric light and special attention has been given to the heating and ventilating exhaust steam being utilised for this purpose under the system of circulation known as the 'Vacuum System'. Special care has also been taken in connection with the sanitary arrangements.

The building has been planned by and carried out under the supervision of Mr H Beswick, the County Architect, who has from time to time conferred with Dr T S Sheldon, and whether regarded from its outward appearance or from its convenient internal arrangements it reflects great credit on his skills as an architect. The Clerk of Works was the late Mr William Longson of Stockport, to whom the Committee are indebted for his assiduous attention during the period the work has been in progress. They regret to say that he died shortly after the completion of the building."

Considering the original plans were drawn up in 1899, this was an example of very forward thinking by all who were involved in its design and planning, being built very much in line with the contemporary medical opinion of the time, with particular regard to the ventilation system, heating system, laboratory, photographic room and operating theatre.

Reorganisation and Appointments

Following the opening of the Annexe a major reorganisation took place, drawn up by the Medical Superintendent, Dr T.S.Sheldon. The broad principles of this were as follows:

1. That all new patients shall be received at the Annexe, where they are classified, and either retained there or transferred to the main building as may be thought desirable.
2. That all sick and infirm patients shall pass through the Annexe, except those suffering from infectious illnesses who will be treated at the Parkside Isolation Hospital.
3. That the Annexe shall be a training school for nurses.
4. That it shall be worked with the Main Building and not be in any way an independent institution.

The staffing of the Annexe necessitated many staff moves, new posts and appointments. Dr.McConaghey, Senior Assistant Medical Officer, was appointed to take charge of the Annexe, residing in the house provided for him (latterly the Medical Centre). His salary was increased from £225 to £250 per annum. Dr H.Dove Cormac, MB BS Madras University, and for three years Assistant Medical Officer at the Wiltshire County Asylum, was appointed to Second Assistant Medical Officer in the main building at a salary of £175 per annum with board, lodging and washing, to increase to £190 after the first year, and £200 after the second year.

Miss Watmough, Head Nurse in post for 4½ years, became Head Nurse for the whole institution, residing in the Annexe with a salary increase from £60 to £70 per annum, rising to a maximum of £80 per annum. Her additional duties included supervision of the kitchens, reception of stores in the Annexe, and to act as Housekeeper for the Annexe.

Miss Longbottom from the West Riding County Asylum, Menston near Leeds, was appointed Second Assistant Head Nurse at a salary of £33 per annum rising to £38 with board, lodging, washing and uniform.

Mr King, Head Male Attendant in post for 17 years, was appointed to take charge of both the male side of the Annexe and main building, with a salary increase from £105 to £115 per annum.

Mr James Mottershead was appointed to Assistant Head Male Attendant, with a salary of £60 per annum plus board, washing and uniform.

Mr Lees, as Clerk of Works, took over the oversight of both the Annexe and main building and had his salary increased from £275 to a maximum of £300 per annum.

Mr Crowdy, the Asylum Engineer, had his salary increased from £120 to £140, rising to a maximum of £150 per annum due to the extra duties incurred by the new steam boilers, electric plant, wiring and fittings.

Mrs Millington, the Housekeeper responsible for superintending the laundry work and making clothing, received a salary rise from £55 to £60 per annum.

Further attendants, nurses and servants were also employed, thus bringing about a substantial increase in staffing levels.

With the completion of the Annexe, the bedding state rose from 806 to 1026 beds and the first patients were received on 20th October 1905. The vacant accommodation was made use of immediately on a temporary basis to patients from other counties until it was required by Cheshire patients. On 26th September 1905, the Committee had agreed to take in 60 patients from other areas. The first of these were from the West Derby Union, Liverpool, consisting of 30 females and 30 males, at a charge of 14s per head per week for three months. Later the Committee signed an agreement with the Committee of the Staffordshire County Asylum at Burntwood, near Lichfield, to receive a number of their patients, not exceeding 40 females and 40 males, at a charge of 14s per head per week. This agreement was entered into for twelve months, having been sanctioned by the Secretary of State.

Original Purpose

No major add on extensions have occurred to the Annexe, apart from the verandah extensions to day rooms and dormitories in the 1920s. During the Second World War, the Annexe was used by the Emergency Medical Services under the control of the military and over 9,000 patients passed through. These included military patients, civilian sick (admitted to release the waiting lists for operations in Manchester hospitals), chronic sick evacuated from institutions in the south, air raid casualties and prisoners of war.

The wards in the Annexe saw varied uses over the years and most of the day rooms and verandahs faced south, many of them providing good views of the surrounding parkland and hills. However, it basically retained its original purpose as an admission and treatment centre, with an excellent laboratory, operating theatre, admission wards, sick wards, convalescent wards and nurse training centre. The theatre and laboratory were still in use up to the early 1970s, and the two admission wards, Female 8 and Male 8, closed towards the end of the 1980s.

East Villa and West Villa

In 1907, two years after the opening of the Annexe, further extensions were suggested on the "Villa System", and plans were drawn up in 1908 for two detached blocks or Villas for pauper patients to be built between the Annexe and Victoria Road, with accommodation for 43 female patients and 43 male; also a detached block or Villa for private patients, to be built on the high ground near Chester Road to the south east of the Annexe, for 79 patients, 39 female and 33 male, plus 4 female and 3 male pauper patients. The architect for all three Villas was Mr Harry Beswick, the County Architect, assisted by Dr T.S.Sheldon, the Medical Superintendent, and the total cost came to £25,000. During their construction, Mr Norman Buckley's father who was an apprentice joiner at the time, travelled from Duckinfield every Saturday morning by pony and trap with the workmen's wages in a Gladstone bag. Having lunched and fed the pony he returned in the afternoon.

In 1908 Back Lane Farmhouse was converted into cottages for use by 8 farmworking patients supervised by a married attendant, and the farmhouse is still standing today, in Priory Lane opposite St Alban's School. Until the 1930s Priory Lane was part of Fallibroome Road running from Broken Cross to Prestbury Four Lane Ends.

The two detached Villas near the Annexe were called East Villa and West Villa and both opened in October 1910. West Villa was for male patients and East Villa, at the time of opening, took in 30 quiet female patients from the Lancashire Asylums Board for two years, at a charge of 14s per head per week. In 1917 West Villa closed due to a shortage of male attendants as a result of the First World War. It later reopened, taking in service patients for a while, then closed again and reopened in 1920 for female patients suffering from colitis. Both Villas throughout the years have been used predominantly as elderly care wards. East Villa eventually became part of the current Jocelyn Solly House, which was probably the last building to be built on the Parkside site under the old health care system and architecturally is in keeping with the original East Villa. The internal facilities and layout of Jocelyn Solly House are excellent, providing for the assessment of the elderly severely mentally infirm patients in pleasant surroundings by a dedicated nursing team. West Villa was demolished in August 1994. Like East Villa it was substantially built with a central water storage tank, floor boards $1\frac{1}{2}$ inches thick and internal ventilation ducts from the tops of the ceilings to ventilators on the roof ridges. Both Villas were constructed by Messrs W.Storrs Sons and Co Ltd.

Uplands Private Villa

The building of the Villa for private patients was approved by the Secretary of State on 29th April 1910. The contractors for the building were J.Gerrard and Sons Ltd, Swinton and a grant was made available from the Council to construct roads, fencing and airing courts. It was formally opened on 22nd May 1912 by Sir James Crichton-Browne (1840-1938), MD FRS, who was previously Superintendent of the West Riding Asylum at Wakefield, later becoming one of the Lord Chancellor's Visitors of Private Patients. The object of Uplands on opening was described as follows:

> *"To provide for private or paying patients the advantages of superior accommodation which are always a feature associated with large County Asylums."*

A few days later 50 patients were admitted at a charge of £1 1s. per head per week. At that time private patients could also be found in the Annexe and main building. Four years later the charge for Cheshire private patients on Uplands had risen to 25s per head per week, and 31s 6d for out-county patients. The Annexe charge for Cheshire private patients was 21s and 25s for out-county. In the main building the charge for Cheshire private patients only was 17s 6d per head per week.

On 31st December 1916 there were 1,317 patients in the hospital; of these 1,046 were Cheshire pauper lunatics, 162 out-county and 109 private patients. Of the 162 out-county, 147 were from Winwick Hospital, which at that time was being used as a Military Hospital, and the charge for these was the actual weekly cost of their maintenance. The charge for Service patients was the normal maintenance rate for Cheshire patients plus an allowance for uniform of 3s 9d per week. Private patients continued to be received upto the formation of the National Health Service in 1948: thereafter the private beds were gradually phased out.

Following the opening of Uplands the kitchen garden was converted into an orchard and a grant of £100 from the County Council was used to purchase fruit trees, whilst land to the west of the clock tower between the Main Building and Victoria Road was converted into a kitchen garden. The stone wall (still standing) running along Chester road was rebuilt by Mr Ball of Macclesfield .Also at this time a year's tenancy of Lower Roewoods farm Birtles Road, was secured at a rent of £60 annually.

Around this time the Committee were paying £1,400 annually in rates, so they decided to apply to the Macclesfield Town Council to extend the gas main and gas lamps in Victoria Road from the main gate to Broken Cross because many of the staff who lived in Broken Cross were walking or cycling home off duty along the unlit road. The Council agreed to this and also awarded a grant of £400 to supply new carpets and furniture for the Medical Superintendent's house, most of which were 40 years old, worn and obsolete.

During 1911, following the completion of East and West Villas, a new much larger cricket pitch was laid out east of East Villa on land that was previously used as a football pitch, and a cricket pavilion was added later costing £76 18s 2d. The staff cricket club was probably formed during 1905, but cricket was first played by patients in about 1884, if not earlier, on the original cricket ground situated to the south east of the hospital church. The cricket pitch still remains and Parkside First and Second Eleven teams are still going strong, with regular matches played throughout the season. The pavilion was demolished when Victoria Road was widened during 1993 and 1994.

View of part of the Annexe shortly after completion in 1905. Water Tower and Hall can be seen in the centre of the picture, with Male Ward 9 to the left and the Medical Officer's House to the right.

Annexe Water Tower, considered worthy of retention due to its unusual roofscape.

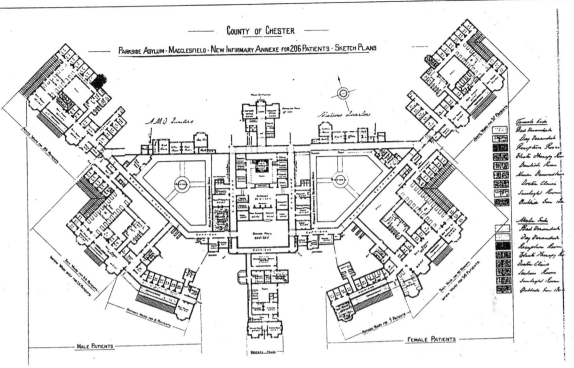

Sketch plan of annexe 1899 by Harry Beswick, County Architect

Senior Assistant Medical Officer's House, Annexe

Male reception ward,
Annexe c1910

Nurses' Lecture Room,
Annexe c1920

The Dining Room, Uplands Private Block.

Both the Annexe and Uplands were used for casualties. This photograph shows a group of stretcher bearers; Nurses Ryan, McMahon, Fergusson, Jordan and Healey

Both male and female 8 wards were usd by Manchester Royal Infirmary during the Second World War. Parkside provided the staff. Seen here outside Male 8, left to right: S N Jones, Sr Keaney (on wall), Deputy Sr White

Aerial view of Annexe and Uplands c1935

Uplands Private block, opened 22 May 1912

CHAPTER 5
The Years of Growth

On 10 February 1915, three fields were purchased from Miss Winifred Vane Barnshaw at a cost of £100 per acre on the west side of the hospital between Chester Road and Fallibroome Road, separated from the hospital estate by a public footpath. The total area of the hospital estate at that time was about 179 acres, including 40 acres of buildings and roads. Of the total acreage, 153 acres were owned by the County and the remaining 26 acres were on annual tenancy held by the Committee. In 1917, a separate entrance was sanctioned from Chester Road to the Medical Superintendent's house and a further 15 acres of land adjoining the estate was rented from the County Council. By 1918 the total acreage under the plough had risen to 80 acres and small allotments were let to 21 staff at an annual rent of 1s per 100 square yards.

During 1919 further expansion was planned in the form of a detached Infirmary Hospital in Victoria Road for 140 beds, but this was later abandoned in 1920. Purchase of more land from the Governors of Macclesfield Grammar School took place in 1921 of 4 acres 2 roods and 35¼ perches at Upton, adjoining the Parkside estate, and in 1922, 12.308 acres were rented from Colonel Becks' Trustees.

The widening of the verandahs on the tuberculosis blocks in the Annexe and alterations to those on Female 8 and Male 8, along with the addition of other verandahs on the side of the dormitories of these two wards, took place in 1923. A portion of each was partitioned off to provide a clinic room. Verandah extensions had also started to take place on some of the wards in the Main Building. The verandah on Female 3 ward was widened. Also that year, an ornamental shelter was built (still standing) in Female 5 airing court.

Despite Parkside being built to relieve overcrowding at Upton Asylum, Chester, Upton continued to expand in a similar way to Parkside with add-on buildings and an Infirmary Annexe. The two Medical Superintendents would meet and exchange views and make visits to see developments in mental hospitals in this country and abroad. Eventually the two hospitals gradually grew apart as a result of the increase in patient population, alterations to catchment areas and Local Authority boundaries. Even so, overcrowding continued to be a problem and in the mid-twenties a special communication was received from the Board of Control calling a conference of the representatives of the Visiting Committees of County and Borough Mental Hospitals in England and Wales. They concluded that having present regard to the rate of increase, present accommodation was equal to two years and as the planning, building and equipping of new extensions usually lasted from five to six years, due regard should be given to this matter by each Visiting Committee.

During 1926 a gymnasium was added to the recreation department in the Annexe and a Chapel of Rest was built onto the Mortuary. Verandah additions to Male 10, Female 10 and Male 9 were completed. The farmland continued to expand with the purchase of Sycamore Farm, Upton on 5th August 1926 in order to house more cattle. A small motor trailer was purchased in 1927 to transport linen from the Annexe to the laundry in the Main Building. Further recreational facilities came about with the construction of new tennis and badminton courts adjoining Uplands for use by private patients and patients from East and West Villas.

By 1928, accommodation was again becoming a problem and discussions took place between Dr Cormac, Medical Superintendent at Parkside and Dr Grills, the Superintendent from Upton Asylum, Chester. The outcome of this was that no further building was advised, but instead further verandah extensions were planned to Wards 3, 5 and 7 in the Main Building, including a double verandah of two storeys on the side of wards Female 6 and 7. All of this work was carried out by the hospital workforce. During 1929 the sewing room in the Main Building was converted into a dining room, a Shoemaker's shop was provided underneath the recently constructed verandah extension to Male 7 ward and the swimming pool was constructed.

Between 1929-1931 efforts were made to reduce the number of patients admitted and to encourage wherever possible the return of patients to the community into the care of relatives and friends. This was attempted by allowing patients out on ground and town parole, giving them more freedom, responsibility and trust - indeed this had always been so even with the very limited means of treatment available at that time. A number of wards adopted the 'open door policy' and a coloured card system was introduced to denote ground or town parole. By 1929, 100 patients were allowed parole beyond the estate.

Despite all these measures the admission rate continued to rise, and in 1931 the Public Assistance Board were informed that only acute and urgent cases could be admitted and no senile chronic imbeciles or idiot patients were to be accepted. As a result of this at the end of 1932 there were only 158 admissions, the lowest for 31 years. This was only a temporary measure, however, and it had been felt for some time that further accommodation was deemed essential. On 6th November 1931 a conference was convened with the Board of Control, represented by Sir Hubert Bond and Mr Brock, along with Mr Cook, Mr Gibbons, Mr Frost, Dr Cormac and the Clerk to the County Council. After much discussion, the conference favoured the building of a new admission hospital and Villas for 500 patients, but due to a number of factors related to the approaching Second World War, it was not until 27th August 1941 that the extensions were finally opened, consisting of six Villas with very unusual green pantiled roofs, but no admission hospital.

In the meantime, due to the growing importance of occupational, recreational and social therapy as a means of treatment, a considerable expansion of the occupational therapy services took place, with the addition of workshops, pavilions, croquet and tennis courts, a bowling green and a small park with pool and aviaries.

On 3rd March 1936, the Knutsford Quarter Sessions finally gave permission for a public footpath running from Chester Road to Fallibroome Road to be diverted in order to enable the proposed Villa extensions to be built.

On 12th May 1937 the Coronation of King George VI took place and many celebrations ensued, including the granting of one day's holiday with pay for all the staff. Bollington Barn House, formerly occupied by the Clerk of Works (Mr Tingay), became the official residence of Dr Stafford, the Hospital Pathologist. With a view to further expansion and to increase the acreage of growing land for vegetables and fruit to supply the increasing hospital population, negotiations were entered into with the trustees of the late Captain Frankenburgh of Upton Priory. These negotiations were finally completed on 30th August 1938 and resulted in the purchase of Upton Priory Estate, consisting of 111 acres including buildings, for £23,000. The buildings included the Mansion House, which was later to be used for a male convalescent villa, housing approximately 20 patients. Large areas of the estate were converted into market gardens, including glasshouses, growing a huge range of horticultural produce for many years.

Meanwhile the proposed Villa extensions on land to the west of the main building beyond the Nurses' Home, began on 16th June 1938, with the estimated date of completion due in 24 months time. Enlargement of the main hall was also recommended and tenders were invited by the County Architect. During the same year an underground telephone cable was run from Chester Road Lodge to replace the unsightly overhead lines running through the grounds.

In 1940, Gorton and Wilson were awarded the contract for the extension of the main hall, but because of the war hostilities this was temporarily postponed and emergency medical accommodation was provided at Parkside by the evacuation of 158 female patients and 97 males from the Annexe and East Villa to other hospitals and alternative accommodation, thus bringing into use 255 beds for the Emergency Medical Services. Air raid precautions received careful consideration, including the building of air raid shelters and the organisation of the fire service. Five sectional huts were purchased, each measuring 50ft by 20ft to release further accommodation for the Emergency Services. Three were used as day rooms, one as a sewing room and the other as a mess room for staff.

Further acquisition of land and property continued during 1940 with the tenancies of Upton Grange Farm and Lower Roewoods Farm obtained by notice to quit, possession taking place on 25th March 1940. Following this a water main was extended from the main building to Upton Priory, and an Assistant Farm Bailiff appointed.

The library in the main building was converted into offices for the Medical Superintendent, and the key room converted into a library. A new petrol pump was installed, along with a coal store for 750 tons.

By 1941, the six 44 bedded villas and an extension to the nurses home were nearing completion along with two villas (still standing) for medical staff, one near the hospital church, and the other near the former main entrance on Chester Road. The six villas, two for women and four for men, plus a kitchen villa, were built on a site of 7.8 acres, 560 feet above sea level west of the Main Building towards Broken Cross. Part of the original wall that encompassed them is still standing, but the villas have since been demolished. The extension to the original Nurses' Home is still standing (October 1995) and was built for 29 nurses. This building supported a cast iron tank containing 7,000 gallons of water being the highest single point on the site. The architect for all the above villas plus Rosemount Out Patients Clinic and two early treatment villas was F. Anstead Browne, the County Architect for Cheshire.

A sum of £3,200 was provided for more air raid shelters throughout the grounds. Most have since been demolished, but some still stand on the north bank of Uplands. A Fire Captain was appointed for the Hospital Auxiliary Fire Service, and staff trained in air raid precaution duties. Macclesfield Borough Fire Brigade were instructed to attend. Surgical instruments were received from America via the Allied Relief Fund for use in the Annexe theatre, which was very busy during the war years.

Despite the war hostilities the Villas extension was formally opened on 27th August 1941. The opening ceremony was performed by the Chairman of the Committee, County Alderman Joseph Cooke, OBE, and Sir Hubert Bond from the Board of Control. Four of the Villas should have been allocated to patients from Upton Mental Hospital, near Chester, which remained overcrowded. However, this never materialised because of staff shortages as a result of the war. It was not until 1943 that five Villas became occupied, and patients from the Nantwich area were also being received in addition to those from East Cheshire. The Committee stated that they were *"willing to take patients from any area in the County which the Public Assistance Committee think most desirable"*. By the end of 1944 all six Villas were occupied, thus raising the normal hospital accommodation to 1,342. On 31st March 1946, the Emergency Medical Hospital in the Annexe was officially closed by the Ministry of Health, and the total hospital accommodation was fully restored to 1,633 beds, but not all of these were ever occupied.

1948 saw the start of a new Pathology Laboratory at West Park Hospital to relieve some of the excessive workload of the Parkside Laboratory, which by that time had become an Area Laboratory and, on 5th July 1948, the hospital started to be administered under the provisions of the National Health Service.

Very little building expansion took place over the ensuing years from 1948, apart from modernisation of the operating theatre in 1953, due to the increased workload provided by the Ear, Nose and Throat Clinic at Rosemount Out Patients Department. Leucotomy operations also arrived for the treatment of anxiety and also as a means of treating some types of schizophrenia. This operation was widely used at the time in all the large psychiatric hospitals, but very quickly fell out of favour due to the poor success rate. General surgery was still being done, along with neurosurgery, particularly thalamotomies for Parkinson's disease. A large number of people were referred from Manchester Royal Infirmary to Cavendish Ward at Parkside, which was previously one of the early treatment Villas. This villa had its own X-ray facilities where careful measurement of the skull was done prior to operation in a complex procedure called stereotaxis.

Staff shortages in the 1950s continued to be a problem and in 1954 there were 1555 beds, but 61 of these were not available, due to shortage of staff. In 1956 two female villas had to be closed and a further two were run by trustworthy patients without nurses. Laboratory techniques were still rather slow, with $3\frac{1}{2}$ hours work for a laboratory technician doing routine admission tests. A Comforts Officer was also appointed in the same year to supervise the various payments administered to patients and by 1955 television sets had arrived on the wards. A full time Librarian had also been appointed and two patients' social clubs were being held, one in the Main Building, the other in the Annexe. The South Cheshire Group opened a new laboratory at West Park Hospital, which considerably eased the work that had been placed on the Parkside Laboratory over the years.

During the mid 1950s and 1960s new treatment methods slowly began to be accepted with the arrival of antibiotics. antipsychotics, antitubercular and anticonvulsant drugs and the hospital long stay population gradually started to decrease during the mid 1960s. Upton Priory Estate was sold off and the farm eventually closed down during the 1970s.

The Industrial Therapy Unit opened in 1966 (now demolished) followed by the Young People's Unit in 1970 (since closed). Neither were of architectural merit, but served the purpose for which they were built with two excellent nursing teams, providing a much needed service for adolescents and work therapy for people recovering from major mental illnesses.

Jocelyn Solly House was probably the last building to be built on the Parkside site under the old health care system, it opened in February 1985 and retains a degree of architectural merit, with first rate provisions for the care and assessment of the elderly, including a day hospital.

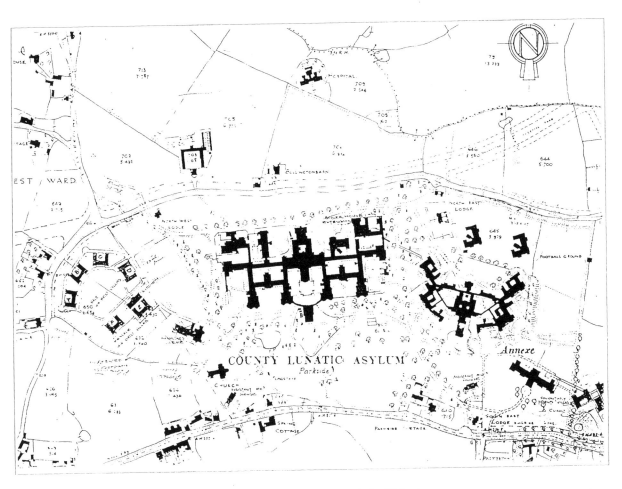

By 1950 the estate had expanded still further.

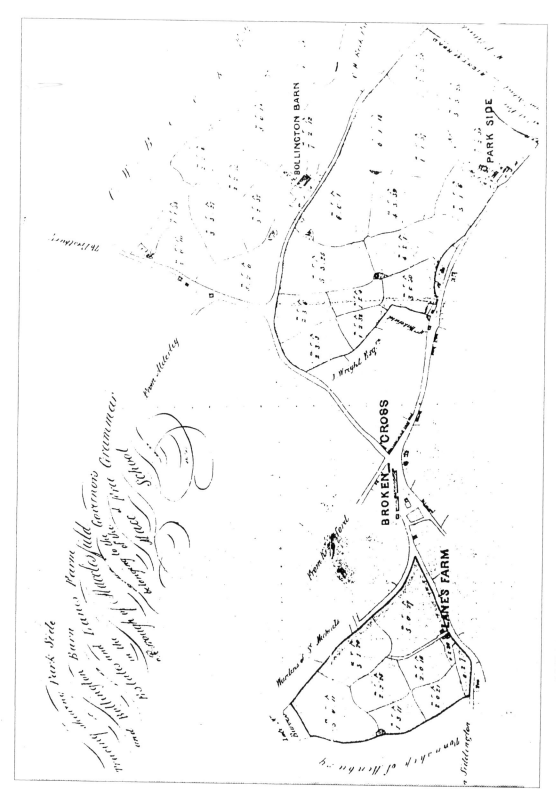

1867 Plan of the original Parkside site. The Lane's Farm estate at Henbury was later abandoned in favour of the Park Side estate at Macclesfield.

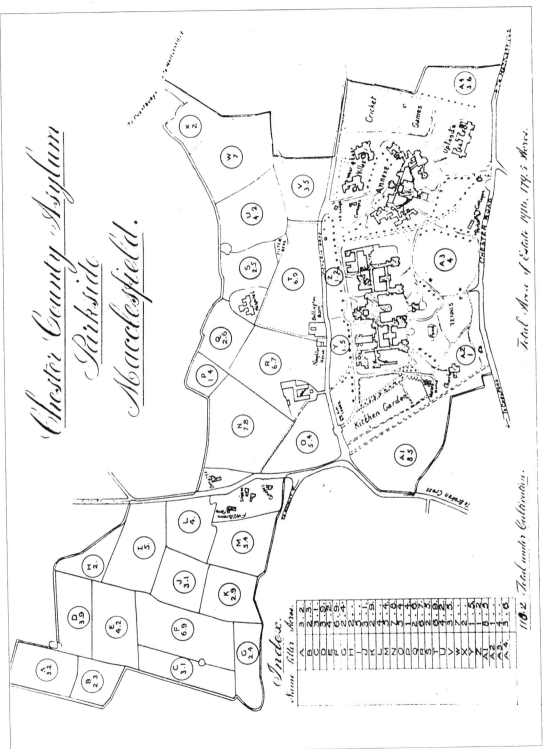

The extent of the estate in 1916.

Aerial photograph c1948

The aerial view shows the hospital at the peak of its development c1948. The Main Building stands central, with the Annexe to the rear, right, and Uplands far right. The farm can be seen S W of the Main Building, over the road. The Villas complex, Nurses' Home and Church can be seen in the foreground. Most of the fields and open spaces have now vanished beneath later development. Many of the hospital buildings have been demolished and further development is in progress.

This photograph, c1962, shows Bollington Barn House on the left, the oldest building remaining on the original site. Parkside Isolation Hospital, later the Nurses' Training School, can be seen in the background.

Extension to the original Nurses' Home, opened 27 August 1941.

CHAPTER 6
Occupational, Social and Recreational Therapy

Organised occupational therapy began at Parkside in 1922 when a determined effort was made to establish it as a method of treatment. Throughout the following ten years a steady expansion of occupational, social and recreational therapy took place and by the mid 1930s it had become a well recognised form of treatment towards full recovery. It would appear that Parkside was one of the first mental hospitals in Great Britain to appoint a full time Occupational Therapy Officer in 1923.

The term 'occupational therapy' was coined by George Barton of Clifton Springs, USA and the first Occupational Therapy College to open in England was Dorset House in Bristol, in 1930. Later a further college opened in Liverpool and Dorset House moved to Oxford. Initially, occupational therapy was done by nurses on the wards but this proved to be unsatisfactory. It meant that the patient was living in the same confined environment 24 hours per day and inevitably unhealthy lifestyles developed. As the method of treatment grew, more specialised full-time training courses were established and it became a profession in its own right. Originally, occupational therapists took the RMPA examinations. At the same time, purpose built occupational therapy units began to appear away from the wards, along with recreational halls, gymnasiums, swimming pools and sports pitches.

Some form of occupational therapy had been done on the wards at Parkside prior to 1922, along with a variety of social events, but for a long time the airing courts had been consistently used as exercise yards and for fresh air treatment. In 1922 a large army hut, measuring 60 feet by 20 feet was erected on the cricket field, and during the day one hundred patients participated in gymnastics, games and other occupations. Dinner and tea were sent down each day from the kitchens. and cake and tea were sold to patients' relatives and friends. The benefits that accrued over time from this therapy were evident in the patients' behaviour, with diminished excitement, more orderly behaviour, improved health, greater trust and confidence in each other and in the staff. This move from the wards and airing courts to the 'outside', as it were, with greater freedom and space, marked a significant turning point, and probably provided the impetus for plans to build purpose built Occupational Therapy Departments and Workshops away from the wards in more spacious surroundings in the grounds. More emphasis was attached to treatment and the word "therapeutic" started to be used.

The Commissioners' report for December 1922 noted that:
"The number of patients usefully employed, judging by prevailing standards, is good ,though a considerably higher proportion of women than men appear to be employed. Whether by the introduction of such occupations as basket, mat and brush making more of the men might be induced to employ themselves, and still more of the women by using their help on the land, I am not sure; I am glad however to learn that Dr Cormac is considering for recommendation to his Committee the appointment of an officer who has. been specially trained in teaching crafts. From war hospital experience, I believe that the appointment of such an Occupational Instructor, perhaps first on one side, as an experiment might prove an economical step as well as a powerful aid to treatment."

In 1923 Miss Myrtle B Hurry, Associate of the Royal College of Music, Manchester, was appointed Occupation and Games Mistress, with a special interest in the therapeutic use of music and musical exercises. Music therapy had only previously been used in mental hospitals in the USA, and in the war hospitals of Great Britain. During the same year a cinematograph was purchased from the Wattendan Company Ltd for £123 5s and fixed in the main hall and a 14-seater charabanc was purchased for the private patients on Uplands ward, and was later used by other patients. Male wards 4, 8 and 10, and female wards 2, 10, 11, 12 and Uplands, were allowed to sit up until 9.30-10.00pm. Practically every ward had a gramophone and piano at this time.

In 1924 occupational therapy was extended to the male patients, with a class of nine, which gradually grew to over one hundred. The Commissioners' report, following their visit in November of the same year, commented about this:

"We are glad to note that an instructor in connection with the occupation of male patients has been appointed. An occupational mistress on the female side has for some time been at work with excellent results, so that it will be seen keen attention is being paid to the occupation of patients, a by no means unimportant item in the treatment of those under care."

By 1925 Sister Dorothy Bavin, a general trained nurse, had been appointed as Masseuse, setting up special baths for hydro and electro-therapy. She also had a certificate in Swedish drill and devised a set programme of exercises to music with two classes per week. In 1927 the hospital Chaplain, the Reverend T.J.Nash, started instruction classes in gymnastics to both patients and staff in the newly constructed gym in the Annexe recreation hall. A swimming pool was also under construction to the west of the Medical Superintendent's House in the main complex. Many wards were equipped with billiard tables and instruction on how to play was given by the hospital Chaplain. In the same year tennis courts, badminton courts, croquet courts and a bowling green were laid out on land adjoining Uplands, for use by patients and staff.

Fifty nine patients were treated in the massage and hydrotherapy department, to which a Turkish Bath, convertible to a vapour bath, had been added. 1928 saw thirty nine patients treated with ultra-violet rays for both mental and physical disorders, and forty seven patients treated with radiant heat, Turkish baths, general massage and needle baths, with some benefit in all cases. There were even 'sunlight treatment baths' situated outside Female and Male 10 wards, near to the entrance doors via Male 9 and Female 12.

During the winter months there were weekly dances, concerts and entertainments by artists from Manchester. The following amateur concert and dramatic societies gave entertainments during the winter months of 1929: The Nomads Dramatic Society, Shell Mex Amateur Players and The Manchester Refined Concert Party.

The combined effects of occupational therapy, the growing use of hydrotherapy and light therapy as a means of treatment in separate departments and in special rooms in the Annexe, led to the need for further accommodation. In June 1931 a new occupation pavilion was built (now demolished) with a floor space of 2,400 feet for both male and female patients. It was situated in pleasant surroundings in the grounds, providing occupation which was looked upon more as recreation than as work. The average attendance was 20 men and 40 women. The Commissioners, in their report for that year, described it as *"a valuable addition to the hospital"*.

In 1932 the Committee converted a four acre field between the main complex and Chester Road into a small park, with a large round shelter, an ornamental pool sporting twelve species of waterfowl, and aviaries containing Java Sparrows, Budgerigars, Turtle Doves, Golden Pheasants and Amethyst Pheasants. The Dovecote was constructed by Mr Fred Moss, Foreman Bricklayer with bricks from the Main Building. It is still standing today on the redeveloped site. These features created much interest amongst the patients. The Occupational Therapy Department continued to expand, and employed its first pupils to train as Occupational Therapists. This was probably one of the first attempts at any form of systematic training for Occupational Therapists in a British mental hospital.

It was from the ranks of the Occupational Therapy Department that Parkside's first Social Worker was appointed, Miss M.McCormac, in 1932. She had previously worked as an Occupational Officer. The new post of Social Worker arose as a result of the recommendation brought about by the Mental Treatment Act of 1930. Miss McCormac gathered together a huge amount of information concerning the patients. She visited the houses of all newly admitted patients every two weeks, establishing a link with the relatives, and reported on their histories, environment and employment prospects for the future. A very positive approach was adopted at this time, especially with regard to employment, and when the patient was finally discharged she plotted their progress, providing detailed after care reports.

It was during 1932 that the World Health Congress held an exhibition in London, and Parkside staged an exhibit stressing the importance of occupational therapy in the treatment regime. A paper read at the Congress defined occupational therapy as follows:
"Occupational therapy is a form of treatment by organised occupation for patients suffering from mental disorders. It is the means of disciplining the mind to give attention to and concentrate on normal things, has a great influence on conduct, and helps to re-establish healthy mental reactions to environments. As a means of helping the mentally sick it is not by any means new. Written records tell us that considerably over one hundred years ago it was considered and commented on, and that good results came from it. As a general organised treatment in mental hospitals it is comparatively new".

In 1933 'talking' pictures were introduced in the main hall, and the installation of wireless sets started to take place in the wards, accompanied by the appearance of radio aerials on the roofs of the buildings. Pianos, of course had been in the wards since the 1890s. The annual sports day in 1933 was attended by over 600 patients.

January 1934 saw the opening of a new occupational pavilion (now demolished) for male patients and the original pavilion of 1931 was used entirely for female patients. The new pavilion was fitted out with joinery benches, and articles such as dinner wagons, tables and useful furniture were made. French polishing was also done, along with repairing of cane seats, tennis and badminton racquets and elementary bookbinding. This pavilion was later extended by 170 feet and housed the Tailor's, Shoemaker's and Upholsterer's Department, which previously had been in the main building. The craftsmen in charge of each department were expected to 'instruct' the patients working with them in their respective trades, as well as carry out general repairs and undertake new work. The Tailor's Department produced trousers, jackets and vests, and the greater part of male patients' clothing was made for many years.

Other crafts included beekeeping, the produce of which was much appreciated, and the installing of a Crown Folio Size Platen Printing Machine provided the means for the hospital to become self-sufficient in the printed word - formerly this service had gone out to contract. A sewing room, bacon curing room, bakery, jam bottling room and vegetable house were added in later years. The Shoemaker's Shop was ultimately to provide the majority of boots, shoes and slippers for the whole hospital. Groups of patients worked on the farm, in the kitchen gardens, and grounds. A small 'counter' was provided in the Annexe Hall where patients could purchase small articles of haberdashery, along with tobacco, cigarettes and sweets.

In 1933 Dr L.C.F.Chevens, Second Medical Officer at Parkside, visited the Provincial Ziekentivis, Santpourt, Holland, to study the intensive application of occupational therapy being undertaken at this hospital by Dr Krouse, the Medical Director. The three chief spheres of occupation and work were the grounds, divisional workshops and central workshops. These provided a series of graded tasks, with the patient perhaps starting in the grounds and then moving into the divisional workshops and finally the central workshops. He noted also that two houses were provided with twenty patients in each, who lived together without nursing supervision. These houses were beautifully decorated in bright colours, made cheerful by English railway posters. Each patient had a separate bedroom in which they were allowed to keep any articles of their own. A coffee house was also provided with a covered-in verandah, where patients could buy tea and cakes on visiting days.

By 1936, 80% of male patients and 81% of female patients were engaged in some form of occupation. Some would be engaged in traditional craft type activities and others would be undertaking work therapy in order to prepare them for eventual discharge. Much of the therapy was directed towards the needs of the hospital rather than the patient, but in its broadest social sense, in terms of community and togetherness, it provided a wide range of different crafts, skills and occupations, and the hospital became a veritable hive of activity. A strong sense of community was created by working together in teams and groups according to each individual's ability, thus creating a sense of mutual responsibility. It was described as being almost like a small town, and within it structures arose which were able to carry the social load for the individual at a time when they were unable or temporarily least able to help themselves due to mental illness. Later on the hospital became almost self-sufficient, with everyone working together towards a common aim - contributing towards its upkeep.

Today this would be frowned upon and interpreted as exploiting the patients or using them as cheap labour, but given the circumstances of the time, the absence of modern day medication, lack of present day mobility, and the determined efforts being made at that time to try and treat and understand mental illness, then one must commend what was being done. An active and contented working atmosphere provides a powerful therapeutic force, installing greater confidence, trust and stability in the patient. Lack of stimulation leads to increasing withdrawal, passivity and lack of volition. When Occupational Therapy first started at Parkside, a selected group of patients were encouraged to occupy themselves as part of the treatment, and this group was compared with another group who were allowed to sit in a chair all day on the ward doing nothing. The prognosis of the first group was much improved with time. They became more alert, active, happier and sociable, whilst the prognosis of the second group remained poor. More recent studies have confirmed those findings, in that the most important single factor associated with improvement in the mentally ill, particularly in schizophrenia, was a reduction in the amount of time spent doing nothing. Conversely, any tasks given must be graded and gradual because over-stimulation may produce too much incoming information which the patient, because of the nature of the illness, is unable to cope with leading to increased agitation or withdrawal.

Sport was also an effective therapy during these growth years. Cricket and football teams were formed and matches played regularly. A league was formed from patients in six wards. Likewise the ladies held netball competitions and gymnastics; physical drill and dancing classes became part of the weekly routine. Trips out to many of the local beauty spots and places of entertainment were greatly enjoyed. A day's fishing at nearby Capesthorne Pool was a popular pastime for many male patients, a good selection of rods being available on Male 10 Ward.

In 1939 a facility was provided for self-caring patients at Rosemount House(now demolished) to the east of the present Rosemount Clinic, along with two Villas for early treatment, one on either side of Rosemount Clinic. Following the purchase of Upton Priory Estate along with the dwellings in 1939, a group of twenty two self-caring patients lived in the Mansion House itself. Part of the Priory still remains at the end of Beck Lane opposite Macclesfield Leisure Centre. Another group of eight patients lived at Back Lane Farm (still standing) opposite St. Albans School.

This gradual move away from the wards and airing courts, with a greater sense of freedom, created within many patients an internal self-discipline which was far healthier and more effective than the old externally imposed discipline of control and restraint within a locked ward. Large numbers of patients assumed greater responsibility and trust, which ultimately led in many cases to their eventual discharge. As a result of these developments in occupational, social and recreational therapy, many visitors from other mental hospitals in this country and abroad came to see and learn about them at Parkside.

With the start of the Second World War in 1939 further developments in treatment were gradually halted, and the Annexe was used as an Emergency Medical Services Hospital. The two early treatment Villas were used as staff quarters. Five sectional huts were erected to release more space on the wards. Beds were moved at different stages into the Annexe and main hall. The hospital became overcrowded and conditions were very austere. Despite the war years a new detached block of six Villas (now demolished) opened on land to the west of the main building at the junction of Fallibroome Road and Priory Lane. This extension was formally opened on 27th August 1941, but it was unable to be fully utilised because of shortage of staff during the war. In the later years of the 1960s and 70s, many 'working' patients lived in the Villas and were employed locally in Macclesfield, Prestbury and Bollington, working in various mills, factories and restaurants.

With the ending of war hostilities, things started to get back to normal and in 1948 the National Health Service was born. The 1950s saw a deluge of new pharmacological preparations which marked a major turning point in the treatment of mental illness. The improvement brought about by the new medication in patients hitherto thought of as untreatable fuelled a further surge forward in rehabilitation, and saw the building of a large number of new centres and units for rehabilitation purposes throughout the country. It heralded a new type of therapy called

'Industrial Therapy'.

One of the first hospitals in the country to pioneer Industrial Therapy training schemes was Cheadle Royal, and in the early 1960s Parkside took part in a study with Cheadle Royal, with the blessing of the Manchester Regional Hospital Board, to assess the effectiveness of Industrial Therapy. The training took place in purpose built workshops within the grounds of Cheadle Royal Hospital, and was promoted widely with a film entitled 'The Right to Work'. Part of the unit at the hospital became a sheltered workshop under the Disabled Persons Employment Act of 1944. It was run as a business and was called Cheadle Royal Industries, known as 'Cheeri' products. The aim was to train long term patients from other hospitals up to the standard which would be required to enable them to be passed by the Ministry of Labour as Approved Sheltered Workers earning an industrial wage, whilst at the same time striking a fine balance between the therapeutic needs of the patients concerned, coupled with an efficient business concern.

The Parkside medical and nursing staff selected 133 long stay patients, from a total of 1,150, whom they thought would benefit from the scheme. They were all carefully assessed and grouped into five groups of varying capabilities and potential. Twenty five were accepted at any one time and lived and worked in a unit of their own at Cheadle Royal. They participated well in the work but also, in a much broader sense, gained greater confidence in themselves and in all aspects of daily living. The scheme proved to be a success and was adopted in other mental hospitals. Later in 1966 Parkside built its own Industrial Therapy Units (now demolished). This particular kind of therapy is still carried out in a ward in the Annexe, although its long term future remains in doubt.

In the early 1960s new treatment methods and social changes evolved and the hospital population started to decline. Upton Priory Estate, comprising 111 acres, had previously been sold off. The farm eventually closed down and the land was sold off in the late 1970s.

During the early 1970s another pioneering scheme was initiated by Parkside in conjunction with the Manchester Business School at Manchester University. The scheme was called 'Progressive Patient Care' and involved the regrouping of a large percentage of the hospital patients according to their level of dependency. The idea was to encourage them to become independent through a series of graded occupational, social and recreational activities. Three tiers of dependency were involved, and as the patient gradually improved they were transferred to the next tier in another ward. The final tier was the pre-discharge ward, where the patients became more or less responsible for themselves, attending to their own medication, washing, ironing, and other self help skills. A large number of patients were discharged back into the community at this time. Other patients who, because of the incapacitating effect of their illness, were unable to return to the community, enjoyed a better quality of life within the hospital service, enjoying annual holidays and participating in the wide range of social, recreational and occupational activities still in tact in the 1970s.

This signalled a new change in direction, and gradually traditional craft type activities played much less of a role in the Occupational Therapy Department. Eventually patients who had been engaged in domestic ward work, work on the farm, artisans workshops and grounds were stopped from doing this. Many patients were happy and contented to be engaged in a variety of work tasks of their choosing which served to increase their self-esteem, confidence and social interaction, giving them a sense of purpose along with a small remuneration. They may not have performed as quickly or efficiently as someone outside the hospital doing a similar job for more pay, and indeed would probably be denied a job because of this, but given the opportunity to work at their own pace within a sheltered and accepting environment, then many chose to do this and were much happier and healthier both mentally and physically. The hospital then employed domestic staff and other grades to carry out tasks formerly done by patients and nursing staff. With a declining hospital population in the 1980s, and the average length of stay for new admissions down to 6-8 weeks in some instances, more modern programmes of care, individually suited to each patient's needs, came into being.

One of the Villas was used for many years as an Alcoholic/Neurosis Treatment Unit, the first such unit in the District. The Community Nursing Service at Parkside was born in 1970 and remains one of the most well established quality services in the country, with a team of highly experienced nurses. The Pennine Day Hospital currently provides an excellent service, with a wide range of therapies, run along modern lines. 1970 also saw the opening of the Young People's Unit, again providing a high quality service with a very specialised team, so necessary for this type of work. Sadly it closed in March 1994.

The Nurse Behaviour Therapists also provide a very specialised form of treatment for such conditions as anxiety states, phobic states, obsessional states and a variety of other psychological problems. This type of therapy has been around for many years, having stood the test of time, being a very useful and practical form of treatment without resort to medication. Similar therapy can be used for many of the lifestyle problems - the so called 'stress related illnesses' that are a phenomenon of present day society.

Heather gardens and sewing rooms c 1947

Female occupational Therapy Unit, built 1931, demolished 1994.

Interior view of the Occupational Thereapy Unit

Interior of the Male Occupational Therapy Unit, built 1934, demolished 1994

Samples of furniture made in the Male Occupation Pavilion
left to right; Mr Manssuer (upholsterer), Mr Stevens (tailor), Mr Nelson (in charge of Occupation room).

List of Articles made in the Male Occupation Workshops during the year ended 31st March, 1936.

Brush, etc., Department.

1144	Brooms and Brushes of various kinds.
59	Door Mats.
5	Screens for wards.
11	Letter Racks.
18	Tables.
5	Stepladders.
150	Coat Hangers.
24	Reading Stands.
6	Curbs.
4	Trolleys—food and laundry.
14	**Stools.**
3	**Book Ends.**
10	**Miscellaneous.**

Tailor's Department.

46	Jackets.
46	Waistcoats.
67	pairs Trousers.
1	Overcoat.
36	Linen Coats.
16	Linen Trousers.

Wire Netting and Tile Making Dept. (Commenced July, 1935).

905¼ yards wire netting, assorted widths and meshes.
3500 coloured smooth rubbed Tiles.

Upholsterer's Department.

35	Box Spring Mattresses.
44	Wool Rugs.
47	Baskets.
62	Laundry Bags.
6	Settees.
5	Breakfast Trays.
20	Strong Rugs.
12	Easy Chairs.
1	Piano Stool.
1	Pouffé.

Bacon Curing, etc., Department. (Commenced January, 1936).

1299	lbs. Sausages.
1205	lbs. Polony.
948	lbs. Brawn.
245	lbs. Lard.
218	lbs. Fish Paste.
2636	lbs. Bacon.

Shoemaker's Department.

57	pairs Men's Boots.
28	pairs Men's Slippers.
26	pairs of Women's Shoes.

Jam Department (females). (Commenced February, 1936).

1208	lbs. Apricot Jam.
1776	lbs. Grape Fruit Marmalade.
253	lbs. Orange Marmalade.
35	lbs. Lemon Marmalade.

List of articles made in the Male Occupation Workshops, year ending 31 March 1936

SHEWING OCCUPATIONS OF MALE PATIENTS.

Department.	Number.
Bakehouse	4
Carpenters	31
Upholsterer	12
Engineer	14
Shoemaker	17
Tailor	6
Bricklayers	5
Painters	4
Clerk's Office, etc.	4
Stores	21
Farm	17
Kitchen Garden	59
Grounds, etc.	50
Barrows	39
Special Occupational Department	12
Wire Netting and Tiles	6
Laundry	8
Kitchens	
Other Employments, including Butcher, Tinsmith, Plumber, etc.	21
Ward work (9 wards)	129
	463

SHEWING OCCUPATIONS OF FEMALE PATIENTS.

Department.	Number.
Laundry	83
3 Kitchens, Sculleries and Mess Rooms	40
Canteen	1
Resident Officers' houses and rooms	9
Nurses' Home	5
Ward work (13 wards)	155
Sewing Room	60
Sewing in Ward and Repairs	20
Special Occupational Department:—	
In Pavilion	106
In Wards	60
	166
Jam making	5
Thread picking	40
Knitting (Machine)	2
Exercise and Re-education classes	44
	630

The main occupations of the patients are shewn above, but many of them are also occupied in other ways, such as Physical Culture, Fancywork, etc.

Main occupations of patients for 1936

Staff enjoying themselves around the swimming pool, shortly after its opening in 1929

Ornamental pond with 12 species of water fowl. The tall gentleman, centre, is the son of Dr Cormac. The avaries can just be seen at the back.

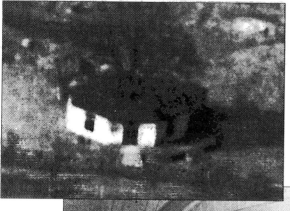

Interior and exterior views of
the circular library, built round
the trunk of a tree.
Before becoming a library it was
a bandstand, then a staff social
club

Female patients from 8/10 wards off to the
seaside, 1960.

Six Ward Football Team.

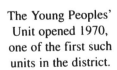

Female 8 Ward
Rounders Team, 1963.

The Young Peoples'
Unit opened 1970,
one of the first such
units in the district.

The Dovecote built c1932 by Fred Moss, using bricks from the Main Building. It was saved from demolition in 1994 by Ann Broadhurst.

Rosemount House, purchased in 1936 to accommodate self caring in-patients.

Hospital Bus for patients' outings. Purchased c.1935. The previous bus was
purchased 3rd January 1923.

Wheelbarrow Squad circa 1930

Wire-netting Room

Patients' Fancy dress Ball in the Main Hall circa 1930

CHAPTER 7
Staffing Matters

In 1843 the first formal psychiatric instruction for nurses was given by Sir Alexandra Morrison at the Surrey County Asylum.

The first attempt at any form of systematic nurse training at Parkside took place in the early 1890s when the Committee reports state that lectures were being given by medical staff to attendants and nurses to prepare them for the Medico-Psychological Association exams. Much esteem was attached to this particular qualification, and it later became the Royal Medico-Psychological Association. It remained one of the main exams for nursing staff up to 1951, when it was eventually discontinued and the General Nursing Council became the main examining body for the state registration of nurses. The General Nursing Council had been in existence for many years and provided for the state registration of nurses, both mental and general, after passing the final examination. The first final examinations for mental nurses were conducted by the General Nursing Council in 1925. The General Nursing Council was later superceded by the United Kingdom Central Council for Nursing, Midwifery and Health Visiting.

An interest in training started to take place in 1895 when 27 attendants and 34 nurses obtained the First Aid Certificate of the St John's Ambulance Association. By 1900 a three year course was established:

1st year	St John's First Aid Certificate
2nd year	St John's Sick Nursing Certificate
3rd year	Medico-Psychological Association Exam for Mental Nursing (selected nurses only)

In 1902 the Nurses' Home was opened for female nurses next to the Hospital Church. It provided accommodation for 32 nurses and was supervised by the Assistant Head Nurse. In 1904 Miss Lloyd, Head Nurse at Parkside, obtained the post of Head Nurse at the City of London Asylum, and a further 13 nurses were awarded the Royal Medico-Psychological Association Certificate, having passed the final exam. They had been trained by Dr McConaghey and Dr Thompson. Miss Watmough was appointed Head Nurse following the departure of Miss Lloyd. The three year system of training remained unmodified up to the 1920s.

With the start of the First World War in 1914, many changes came about, the chief of which was a shortage of male staff and arrangements affecting pay and conditions, due to social changes and the general welfare and rights of people.

Night attendants were allowed 48 nights off duty per year, instead of 2 nights per month for 8 months and 1 night off per month for the remaining four. The annual leave was reduced from 16 to 14 days. Due to the shortage of male staff who were on active service or in munitions, the employment of female nurses on the male wards started to take place for the first time, and vacant posts were filled by women or men over army age. Miss Edith M.Walters from Cardiff City Mental Hospital was appointed to the male side of the hospital as Assistant Matron.

Following the opening of Uplands on 22nd May 1912, and just before the start of the

Great War, a major staffing reshuffle occurred and the number of men applying for some of the key posts was very high. The post of Storekeeper was advertised and the Committee received 425 applications for the job. Six were shortlisted for interview by the Committee, and the successful applicant was Mr A.T.Newell of Macclesfield, Quartermaster, 7th Battalion Cheshire Regiment. The post of Clerk of the Hospital was also advertised and 241 applications were received. Again six were shortlisted and Mr W.G.F.Tingay was appointed, having previously worked as Assistant Clerk and Steward at the West Sussex County Asylum. The post of Clerk of Works was awarded to Mr H.Kelly of Macclesfield, following 118 applications.

With the cessation of hostilities in 1919, the number of staff who had seen active service stood at 66, and 26 staff returned to their former duties. Attendant F.Slack returned to duty on 27th January 1918, unfit for further military service. Stores Clerk, Acting Staff Sergeant G.D.Stafford, AOC, British Salonica Forces, was mentioned in dispatches, for gallant conduct and distinguished service. Attendant William Davenport was killed in action on 27th June 1917. Dr C.K.Smith returned from the RAMC on 26th January 1915, and Storekeeper Captain A.T.Newell was awarded the Military Cross for distinguished service in the field. These were indeed difficult years for all the staff of the hospital, but despite the war, further progress and developments continued, with advances in nurse training, occupational therapy and social conditions.

Peace celebrations were held on 19th July 1919 with a variety of events taking place in the hospital. In the same year, the artisans' working week was cut from 54 to 49 hours, and an extra day off per week was granted to nurses and attendants. An increase in salary was awarded to office staff, along with an improved scale of wages for female staff. The National Asylum Workers Union put in for a 48 hour week, a minimum commencing wage for attendants, nurses, laundry and kitchen staff of £2 per week, a War Bonus of 25s per week, plus a pension after 25 years service of $1/40$th of each year's wages, irrespective of age. As a result of these changes the charges were increased for the Cheshire Unions. The title of 'Sister' was given to those Charge Nurses who held the Final Nursing Certificate. By this time 23 female nurses were employed on the male side with four male wards staffed entirely by female staff, with much success.

The years immediately following the war saw a rising hospital population and difficulty with recruitment of staff, necessitating changes in pay and conditions. A new scale of pay and conditions was started in 1923 when the 60 hour week was increased to 66 hours, and annual leave was reduced from 28 days to 21 days. New male staff wages were reduced from 40s per week down to 34s per week. The reduction for Female staff was 20% lower than males. The idea behind these measures was to reduce the number of staff required and the negotiations were carried out and eventually agreed upon by the Mental Hospital Association and the National Asylum Workers Union.

By 1923 25% of men and 18% of women held the RMPA certificate and three Head Nurses were giving practical demonstrations to probationer nurses. A three year training programme agreement was reached for all new probationer nurses which stipulated that they pay a deposit of 5 guineas (£5 5s), returnable on satisfactory completion of training, although this deposit would be forfeited if they failed to attend the training lectures. Prior to this the probationers had to pay £30 if they broke their contract, but in practice this never worked, so the fee was reduced to 5 guineas. Arrangements were made in 1925 for four Sisters to go for general training, and in each year following two more were allowed to go. Each received £50 per annum while training and signed an agreement to return and remain in the service of Parkside for a period of 4 years. At that time the title of Head Nurse applied to officers between the rank of Assistant Matron and Sister, and this was later replaced with that of 'Matron's Office Sister'. The hours of duty worked by probationer nurses at that time were 58 hours per week, with $10^1/_2$ hour days. Certificated nurses were given an additional week's leave. Working and convalescent patients were allowed to stay up until 10pm, and in these wards no nurses were on duty following the departure of the day nurse at 7.30pm.

Following the introduction of the 5 guinea fee to retain probationers in October 1923, 29 of the original 30 staff remained in employment and were found to be much more satisfactory. Also during this time the diet was improved for the staff and an additional meal was provided when going off duty at 7.30pm. The bedrooms were better furnished and more comfortable, and the Sisters were provided with mess rooms and sitting rooms. Recreation was available in the way of tennis, badminton and dancing, but the Medical Superintendent, Dr H.D.Cormac, wrote in his report for 1925:

"This can, however, be overdone, in the case of the probationer, as it tends to distract her attention from work. She has to be made to realise that she has entered for a three year course of hard study and serious training for a serious profession and that she has not come to enjoy herself and do as little work as possible".

Gradually progress started to be made and the old idea that little or nothing could be done to hasten the recovery of patients began to die out. New treatments, research and improved training programmes for nurses, fuelled a period of great inquiry and discovery. Despite this the hours of work remained long and hard compared to today's conditions.

By 1929 a course of lectures, tutorials and practical demonstrations had become firmly established and, combined with the three year course of training, was to provide the basic pattern of nurse education at Parkside for the next fifty years, modified accordingly with further advances in nursing and treatment.

The first year's training consisted of anatomy, physiology and hygiene lectures, given by Dr H.D.Cormac and Dr H.Fox. Tutorials were given by Miss J.Killough, Assistant Matron, and Sister Dunkerley (Acute Ward), and practical demonstrations by Miss C.M.Moore, Assistant Matron.

The second year of training was as follows: Physical diseases and treatment, by Dr L.C.F.Chevens; Tutorials given by Sister Walmsley (Male Sick Ward) and Senior Staff Nurse Barton (Female Sick Ward); Practical demonstrations by Sister Kennelly (Female Sick Ward).

The third year of training consisted of: Mental disorders and their treatment by Dr G.G.Parkin; Anatomy of the nervous system by Dr H.D.Cormac (Medical Superintendent); Tutorials by Sister Freeman (Female Admissions); Practical demonstrations by Miss Peden (Assistant Matron). The Sisters who took the tutorial classes also attended lectures given by the Medical Officers, and were responsible for ensuring the attendance of the probationer nurses at the lectures. Many nurses who had already passed their final examination also attended the lectures in order to keep themselves up-to-date.

In 1927 twelve nurses and three attendants passed the RMPA final examination, and three silver medals were awarded. Twenty nurses and six attendants passed the preliminary examination. The total number of female nurses holding the final certificate was 42%, while 29% had passed the preliminary examination. This was claimed to be a record, not having been exceeded in any other mental hospital. By this time nurse lecture rooms were well established in the Annexe and were equipped with epidiascopes (a type of projector), anatomical models and instruments. Treatment rooms were fitted out for massage, radiant heat, light treatment and Turkish baths.

In 1928 Miss Jane Mottershead was presented with the MBE by King George V for her services to nurse training and education at Parkside, the first such honour to be bestowed on a purely Mental Trained nurse. At that time many senior nursing posts in mental hospitals went to general trained nurses and Dr H.D.Cormac, throughout his Medical Superintendency, fought long and hard to gain greater recognition for mentally trained nurses at Parkside. He was to write in his report for 1931:

"It is my firm conviction that it is right and possible for every mental nurse to acquire all the knowledge and skill necessary in a mental hospital at a mental hospital, and that such training as is given at Parkside is of sufficiently high standard to render many quite capable and fit to hold the higher posts of Assistant Matron and Matron in a mental hospital. Incidentally, I may mention that several major operations, including abdominal, were performed during the year and that in all cases the patients were successfully nursed by our own staff".

In 1931, 83% of male nurses were in post for over five years, compared with 69% in all mental hospitals, and 37% of female nurses compared with 26% in all mental hospitals. Following 37 years' service, Miss Jane Mottershead MBE retired in 1932, and the Jane Mottershead Medal was founded to be given for exceptional merit in nursing. After the retirement of Miss Mottershead, Miss Moore was appointed to Matron Examiner for the RMPA examinations. In 1934 the Annexe employed 105 female nurses, 17 of whom worked on the male wards, and of these 61% were trained certificated, and 56 attendants, 45% of whom were certificated. By 1938 141 nurses had been trained since 1918 and successfully passed their final exams, and since 1921 40 attendants had passed the final exams and of these 34 still remained in post. Throughout that time nine passed with distinction.

Salaries for clerical staff were increased in 1933 for those who passed the Preliminary and Final Examinations of the Incorporated Association of Clerks and Stewards of Mental Hospitals.

Prior to the National Health Service, the children of staff up to the age of fourteen years received free medical treatment from Parkside's own Doctors. Children could also attend the pictures in the main hall on Friday night, use the swimming pools and various sports pitches. Family functions became regular events, the annual Christmas parties and pantomines were always well attended - and if romance blossomed amongst staff they could be married free of charge at the Church of St Catherine Birtles by the hospital Chaplain, the Reverend Canon T.J.Nash.

Other perks included one shilling extra per week for members of the staff orchestra.

Artisans building the water storage tank in 1929 worked in appalling weather conditions so they were paid one shilling a week extra 'dirt money', by Dr Cormac, Medical Superintendent. Painting the hospital was a perpetual task, taking fourteen painters fourteen years to complete the whole estate.

Following the start of the Second World War in 1939, all further developments in treatment and training had to be slowed down. The whole of the Annexe was used as an Emergency Medical Station run by the military and all resources were directed into caring for the sick and wounded. Many staff were trained in anti-gas and air raid precautions, with volunteers recruited from the artisans' department and nursing staff. A Fire Captain was appointed and all grades of staff volunteered to be fire watchers. The clock tower and Annexe water tower had fire observation windows built into the roofs which remain to this day. Many patients were trained by staff to act as lookouts, taking their share in the staff fire rota.

At the end of the Second World War, sick and injured civilians continued to be cared for in the Annexe for a further two years. The Emergency Station finally closed on 31st March 1946. A considerable number of war casualties were transferred to nearby Capesthorne Hall, for a further period of convalescence. The Annexe was then cleaned up and renovated by the hospital staff and eventually the whole of the hospital was restored to its former bedding capacity of 1633 beds, the highest recorded since opening; this number was never exceeded during the remaining years of its life.

The Rushcliffe Report, which had come into effect on 1st October 1944, brought about a complete revision of the salaries of nursing and other staff and had been long awaited. In the meantime, Dr H.D.Cormac continued his struggle to gain greater recognition and credibility for mental trained nurses, at which time there was an acute shortage. He wrote in his report for 1946, with special reference to female nurses:

"Even with the new wage increase, a modern Nurses' Home and specialist training facilities, women can hardly be expected to enter the mental nursing services when, after passing the final exam of the RMPA or GNC, they are told that they need not expect promotion to higher posts in the service unless they proceed to a further course of training in a general hospital, while on the other hand nurses with a general training are often appointed to the position of Assistant Matron in a mental hospital without any knowledge of, or training in, mental nursing. I have yet to discover why general training fits a nurse at all for mental hospital work. My experience with these women is exactly the reverse."

In 1948 a number of nursing staff were sent to other hospitals to gain experience in insulin treatment, which was starting to be used more frequently at that time. This practice was later rejected due to the poor success rate.

During 1951 the RMPA exam was discontinued and the General Nursing Council Examination became the recognised qualification. By 1953, a national shortage of trained nursing staff was becoming evident and the General Nursing Council was being urged to address this problem. This state of affairs persisted for several more years and nursing staff at Parkside worked huge amounts of overtime. There was a very low intake of student nurses, and many part time and untrained staff were taken on. Many of these came from the local silk industry which at that time was starting to decline. The extent of the problem was highlighted during a visit by the Commissioners in the mid-50s when they found Female 6 Ward to have 62 patients, 30 of whom were in bed, 5 suffering from typhoid, 10 with epilepsy, and one who was suicidal, and only two nursing staff on duty. In order to address this problem the nursing cadet scheme was introduced at Parkside in 1954 to attract school leavers into the nursing profession. This met with some degree of success, and many of the cadets recruited into the hospital at that time remained in its employment, becoming long serving and loyal members of the hospital staff.

Another measure adopted was the carrying out of an extensive recruitment campaign, spearheaded by Matron Parkinson and the Regional Nursing Officer. They made several trips abroad visiting France and Italy to interview young women with a view to nurse training, and this was sponsored by both Governments. They also visited Ireland and the British West Indies. Some of the staff who took up the offer at the time remain in the employment of the hospital in 1995.

The third measure to eventually be adopted was the establishment of a well equipped Nurse Training School at Parkside by converting the old Isolation Hospital into suitable accommodation. Preliminary training had previously been done at West Park Hospital. The opening of the Nurse Training School meant that the whole of the nurse training could be done in one building on the Parkside site. This marked a significant step forward and one which Dr.H.D.Cormac had strived to achieve for many years prior to his retirement in 1947. Nursing Auxiliary training was also done in the same building, along with refresher courses. Later on the lecture room in the Annexe (latterly the Physiotherapy Department) was used for many years, providing a meeting place for all disciplines including the local General Practitioners, Social Workers, Nursing Staff and others. These lectures and case presentations were always well attended and in most instances it was, 'standing room only'.

On 16th May 1954, Mr Fairhall resigned from his post as Chief Male Nurse, after 40 years service, and Mr Frank Willoughby, formerly Deputy Chief Male Nurse at Helleston Hospital, Norwich, was appointed on 1st July 1954. Miss C.M.Moore, Matron, resigned on 25th July 1955, after 44 years service, and Miss A.C.Parkinson, formerly Deputy Matron from Bracebridge Heath Hospital, was appointed on 17th August 1955.

From the mid-50s, the Nurse Training School gradually became well established, with a growing reputation for good standards and an excellent team of Tutors. Nurses from Parkside were well sought after by other hospitals and large numbers of staff were trained most thoroughly over the three year course for both the Hospital and State examinations. Many remained at Parkside, giving many years of unstinting service; others went on to take up posts of responsibility in other hospitals, both in this country and abroad.

Two more nursing staff were to be awarded the MBE: Attendant Fred Marshall for his work in initiating habit training on Male 4 Ward and Geoffrey Kirton for his services to nurse education at Parkside.

Nurse training for the three year Registered Mental Nurse course and the two year Enrolled Nurse course probably reached its peak during the 1960s and 70s, with three intakes per year. Coupled with advances in treatment, particularly pharmacological ones, these were indeed exciting times. March 1974 saw 101 student and 40 pupil nurses undergoing training, and as recently as 1976 the hospital still had 36 wards open with a total of 989 beds. At this time the operating theatre in the Annexe was still in use, and was kept busy throughout the week with both general surgery and neurosurgery taking place. Cavendish Clinic, currently next to Rosemount clinic, was used for neurological patients from Manchester Royal Infirmary. The hospital still retained a remarkable degree of self sufficiency in this respect, and at one time there was talk of a combined four year training course leading to both RMN and RGN, such was the experience available.

The 1980s saw the Government initiative to gradually close down the large County Mental Hospitals, and eventually the Nurse Training School was closed at Parkside. The late 1980s brought in a new way of training nurses called Project 2000; this was heralded as the only change in nurse education since the 1920s, *"born of the need for change on educational grounds, the growing demand of the service area, the need to recruit and retain highly qualified staff and the demographic changes which project the health care needs into the 1990s and beyond".*

In practice the mental illness branch of Project 2000 has not lived up to its original expectations, partly as a result of the speed of recent changes, not only involving the way nurses are trained but the way in which the current health care system is funded and administered and the sense of flux that has been created. The skilled Registered Mental Nurse is fast disappearing in the culture of redundancy hitting the large county mental hospitals. A similar fate happened to the RMPA certificated nurses in the 1950s following the formation of the National Health Service in 1948. The trained mental nurses left in the system come under increasing pressure to embark upon managerial and business type courses far removed from the nursing for which they were originally trained. Along with this comes a new breed of social carer rather than a nurse; less expensive, three weeks training and if the budget will allow perhaps a National Vocational Qualification later on. Ultimately all future training will depend on the provider's ability to provide education and training if there is a market for it.

The impact of these changes remains to be assessed by the historians of the future, as does the move towards the social care of the mentally ill in smaller units in the community. Their ability to become part of a community and that community's acceptance of them will be all important as opposed to being in the community yet still remaining isolated. Adequate training will be required for the new breed of carers who will look after them as well as much education of the general public, which is still inadequate at the present time. Likewise research into the causation of mental illness, particularly schizophrenia, must not be neglected; there have been few major advances in treatment since the antipsychotics were discovered in the 1950s, followed by the antidepressants in the 1960s. Psychiatry remains a relatively young and inexact science and much work remains to be done into the causation and understanding of mental illness.

Recruitment leaflet for nurses c1960

A NURSING CAREER AT

Parkside

Hospital

A SOUND THREE-YEAR TRAINING COURSE IN NURSING

IN IDEAL COUNTRY SURROUNDINGS

13 WEEKS PAID HOLIDAY DURING TRAINING

PLUS THE FRIENDLY COMPANY OF FELLOW STUDENT NURSES

MEDICAL DIRECTOR : Dr. R. H. BOARDMAN

The Hospital

There is a wide, fuller life awaiting both men and women in Psychiatric Nursing and especially at PARKSIDE where much has been done to make the nurse's life one of a happy community. Read here about our work, training and relaxation and we feel sure that you, too, will be interested in . . . A nursing career at Parkside Hospital.

All forms of modern treatment for psychiatric patients are given. The Hospital is equipped with its own Pathological laboratory, Operating Theatre, Electroencephalographic Department, a Neurosurgical unit, and an X-ray Department. Plans are going ahead for an Adolescent Unit. As one of the pioneers of the treatment of psychiatric illness by organised occupation and rehabilitation, Parkside is still in the vanguard of this branch of healing therapy and has special centres with skilled instructors covering all forms of occupation.

Parkside accommodates about 1,400 patients and with active treatment, this number is being reduced. This reduction can be speeded up with the help of nurses. If you are desperately keen to take up pschyiatric nursing, we are desperately keen to have you.

Training

(To qualify for state registration in psychiatric nursing).

The complete course of training is of three years duration under the direct supervision of the Matron and Chief Male Nurse.

Points of entry are in March, July and November of each year when students attend the Nurse Training School for an Introductory Course of six weeks' duration after which ward duties are undertaken.

Further study days are arranged during the year, when lectures and clinical demonstrations are given by members of the medical or tutorial staff.

All tuition is given during duty hours.

State Registered Nurses may take a special 18 month course of training for admission to the psychiatric register and nurses who are registered in the nursing of the mentally subnormal a twelve month course.

Enrolled Nurse Training

For those who wish to be nurses of a more practical nature there is now training for the Roll.

This is of two years duration, and although it is less academic than training for the Register, classroom tuition is organised which is closely allied to the practical experience which will be gained on the wards.

This is followed by an assessment which may be taken in either March or September of each year, so long as the pupil has completed at least 18 months training. On the successful completion of this the candidate may apply for admission to the Roll of Nurses at the end of two years.

At Parkside Hospital, either of the afore-mentioned schemes of training may be undertaken.

Conditions of service are continually improving, and the training allowances and subsequent salaries are quite substantial, with good prospects for further promotion for candidates of the right calibre.

Although we are required to perform a 24-hour service to the patient, hours of duty are not long and there is adequate time-off arranged. The working week will be reduced to 42 hours by the end of 1965, but it is hoped to bring about this reduction before this time.

Annual leave is liberal, starting with four weeks in each of the first and second years, but increases to five during the third year.

All posts are superannuable in accordance with the N.H.S. Superannuation Scheme.

Psychiatric Nursing

Nursing of all kinds is primarily a vocational profession, and calls for the very best in each one of us. Nowhere is this more in evidence than in the modern psychiatric hospital.

Today, treatments have advanced at such a pace that no longer is the patient condemned to years of incarceration, but can be well on the way to recovery within weeks, or even days, after admission to hospital. Patients, who a few years ago were regarded as social outcasts, can now become useful citizens either inside or outside the hospital, and no profession is more rewarding to the person who has an inherent desire to help others.

There are very few people, providing they have the right personality, who cannot be fitted into the therapeutic climate of the psychiatric hospital. Training for this work can be fitted into two categories:

All training is under the jurisdiction of the General Nursing Council, and may be for the Register or the Roll.

Training for the Register is of three years duration, and for this a satisfactory educational attainment is necessary.

List of nurses awarded the RMPA Certificate between 1918-1937

(The names of those who have left the Hospital are in italics.)

Year.	Nurses.	Attendants.
1918.	Annie M. Craib.	
	Jeanie Killough	
	Annie M. Peden (Deputy Matron).	
	Sarah J. Leigh.	
	Minnie Leigh.	
	Ruth Dunkerley.	
	Ellen Mary Rudd.	
	Amy Rose.	
	Winifred M. Green.	
	Mary A. Frost.	
1919.	Celia M. Moore (Matron).	
	Minnie Wigglesworth.	
	Elizabeth Ellen O'Connor. (Asst. Matron).	
	Mary Kate Lynes.	
1920.	Annie James.	
	Martha Ann Ford.	
	Edith Beach.	
	M. S. Baggaley.	
	M. L. Bloor.	
	A. Bracegirdle.	
1921.	Hilda A. Belfield.	Harry Bannister
	Frances Moss.	Ernest Young.
	Catherine Thompson (Birch).	
	Kathleen Hughes (D).	
1922.	Mary Pearson	William B. Buxton (Deputy Head Attendant).
	Laura Duffin.	Harold E. Fairhall (D) (Occupation Officer).
	Alice Belbin.	Harry Baron
		Wm. Osbaldeston.
1923.	Stella Muriel Bailey.	Joseph Mollard.
	Mabel Irene Dyne.	John Henry Crouch.
1924.	Adela G. Cox.	Harold Bailey.
	Blanche Naylor.	Arthur L. Hatton.
	Harriett Shaw.	Frank Ashley.
1925.	Alice Winstanley.	
	Edith Tomlinson.	
	Hannah Allen.	
	Annie McGurrin.	
	Louisa Careless.	
	Edith Horton (Davies).	
	Eva D. Gerecht.	
1926.	Caroline O'Donohue (D).	Charles H. Nield.
	Kate Drugan.	Albert G. Davies.
	Mary K. Quinn.	Jas. L. Leighton.
	Mary L. Edwards.	
	Catherine Hughes.	
	Eleanor C. Long.	
	Mary J. Rathbone (Healy).	
	Mary A. Page.	
	Lilian O'Connor.	
	Florence Hopkins.	
	Hilda Jones.	
	Kathleen Hughes.	
1927.	Maude A. Garland.	Eddie Shufflebotham.
	Annie Dora Jones.	James Dunkerley.
	Dorothy J. Barton.	
	Alice Keaney.	
	Bridie Moran (D).	
	Margaret May Bolgere (Morgan)	
	Dorothy Ann Price.	
	Blodwyn E. Pritchard.	
	Henrietta Hughes.	
	Annie Cotter.	
	Nora White.	
1928.	Lizzie Hammersley.	Sam Wrigley.
	Gladys Horobin.	Henry Dobson.
	Lilian Daisy Pitts.	Vincent M. Roberts.
	Annie Torrens (Asst. Matron)	John Cornes.
	Maggie E. Kraney.	Ernest Mellor.
	Ethel Cahill.	
	Esther Seymour.	
	Mary Beaver.	
	Ruth Miles.	
	Mollie Owens.	
	Agnes Moore.	
	Margaret Mary Healy.	
	Winifred M. Bradshaw.	
	Rose Ann Brady.	
1929.	Ruby Shaw.	Stanley Lea Royle.
	Brigid Quinn.	
	Naomi Jones.	
	Ellen Maxwell.	
	Mary Barker (Owens).	
	Ellen Phelan.	
	Rose Ann Kelleher.	
	Brigid Brady.	
1930.	Marjorie Isobel Pitts.	William Smith.
	Mary Josephine Killen.	Daniel Bradley.
	Mary Kate Harte.	Leonard Winterburn.
	Margaret M. Black.	Walter Crossley.
	Bessie M. Beaufoy.	William Richardson.
	Sarah Elizabeth McConkey	
	Kate Maud Webb (D).	
	Bessie Delaney.	
	Ruth Shiela Garside.	
	Mary Maggie McDonnell.	
	Minnie Rogers.	
	Rosemary Gilroy.	
	Annie Dickinson.	
	Eleanor E. Etheridge.	
	Marjorie A. Boulton.	
1931.	Blanche Forster.	Thomas William Smith.
	Bridget Harte.	Albert Edward Ward.
	Jane Hamilton Higgins.	
	Mary Clarke.	
	Mamie McGurrin.	
	Bridie Owens	
	Elizabeth McDonnell.	
1932.	May Florence Bayliss	Ernest G. Gordon.
	Margaret Walsh.	Owen H. Jones.
	Bridie Josephine Linnane.	
	Genevieve Mary Powell.	
	Bridget Cremin.	
	Mary Ann Mullally.	
	May Forrest Wheeler.	
1933.	Kathleen Davis.	Leonard Beech.
	Kate Phelan.	Ernest Cockayne.
	Margaret Jane Mullally.	
	Agnes Barbara Earnshaw.	
	Elizabeth Brown.	
	Rose Tessie O'Kane.	
	Jane Edwards Lewis.	
	May Gavin.	
	Gladys Cockitt.	
	Mary Anne Dolan (D).	
	Helen McBeath Gray.	
	Jane Elizabeth Higgins.	
1934.	Margaret Conn.	William Davison.
	Ada Duffield.	Thos. A. Amesbury.
	Ivy Brown	Alexander Stubbs (D).
	Josephine Mackin (D).	Ralph Lonsdale.
	Mary R. Kerr.	
	Maud White.	
1935.	Mary E. Flannagan.	William E. Nixon.
	Kathleen Kerr.	William Ball.
	Myfanwy Thomas.	John W. Thompson.
	Alice Mary Skelhorn.	
	Florence A. Walker.	
	Edith Bradford.	
	Mona S. Barras.	
	Clara J. Walker.	
	Elizabeth Mary German.	
	Eva McConkey.	
1936.	Marice Merlin McCormick.	Charles H. Duckworth.
	Alice L. Mitchell.	Sidney Holden.
	Eileen M. J. Bradley.	William Clarke.
	Matilda Johnston.	James Kemp.
	Eira W. L. Roberts.	
	Margaret A. M. Keeling.	
	Robina Y. Niblock (D).	
	Eileen M. T. Harverson.	
	Margaret Hall.	
	Sarah A. Davenport (Jones)	
	Christina McClelland.	
	Annie E. M. Callister.	
	Martha McClung.	
1937.	Rosie P. Jones.	Frederick D. Marshall.
	Lavinia Rowland.	William E. Jones.
	Annie M. Roberts.	Frederick W. Abrahams.
	Cicely Williams.	William H. Perkins.
	Yvonne C. E. Bradbury.	Robert G. Jones.
1938.	Marjorie Read.	Richard Watkin
	Daphne A. Cooney	Sidney Hall
	Elizabeth E. James	William Lawrence
	Phyllis M. Moore	John H. Pratt
		Jack Gawthrope
		Stanley M. Davidson

Three others members of the Staff passed the Examination prior to commencing duties at this Hospital.

(D)—passed with distinction.

CONDITIONS OF SERVICE

TABLE I.—STUDENTS IN TRAINING BEFORE THE 1st JANUARY, 1949. RATES OF TRAINING ALLOWANCES PAYABLE FROM THE 1st SEPTEMBER, 1948.

(This table covers all female student mental nurses and resident male student mental nurses).

	Annual cash training allowance (including responsibility allowance). Dependants' allowances to be added where applicable.	Value of Emoluments	Living-out allowance	Total value training allowance and emoluments or living-out allowance.
1st year	£130	£100	£100	£230
2nd year	£140	£100	£100	£240
3rd year	£155	£100	£100	£255

In addition, the following proficiency allowances will be payable.

(a) £20 on completion of the second year of training or the passing of the preliminary examination, whichever is the later.

(b) £30 on completion of the third year of training or the passing of the final examination, whichever is the later.

TABLE II.—STUDENTS ENTERING TRAINING ON OR AFTER THE 1st JANUARY, 1949. ANNUAL RATES OF TRAINING ALLOWANCES PAYABLE.

(This table covers also as from the 1st September, 1948, male non-resident students previously paid on a non-resident basis).

	Annual cash training allowance (including responsibility allowance). Dependants' allowances to be added where applicable.	Payment to hospital where board and lodging provided.
1st year	£230	£100
2nd year	£240	£100
3rd year	£255	£100

In addition, the following proficiency allowances will be payable.

(a) £20 on completion of the second year of training or the passing of the preliminary examination, whichever is the later.

(b) £30 on completion of the third year of training or the passing of the final examination, whichever is the later.

Nurses' salaries 1948-1949

The Royal Medico-Psychological Association.

This is to certify that ALEXANDER STUBBS having been duly trained at .... according to the Regulations of the Association has shown in examination Proficiency in Mental Nursing and that he has passed the examination With Distinction.

Signed .... Chief Examiner.

Countersigned .... Superintendent.

.... President.

.... Registrar.

Dated ....

RMPA Certificate with distinction awarded to Alexander Stubbs in 1934. *Courtesy Mr A Stubbs*

Annual Nurses' Prize giving Ceremony May 1968
Front Row L to R: Miss F.Potts (Matron); Mr.F.Willoughby (Principal Nursing Officer);
Mr.J.Solly (Committee Chairman); Mr.D.Ferris (Silver Medallist); Dr.R.Boardman (Medical
Superintendent); Miss M.Hill (presenting prizes);---------- ----------;
Mr.E.Cockayne (Chief Male Nurse); Mr.G.Kirton. MBE (Principal Tutor).

Nurses' prize giving ceremony
outside the training school c1960.

Married man's Football Team late 1930s
Back row L to R: ----, Bert Ruffles, Joe Worthington,
George Nixon, Harry Groves, Harry Hodgkinson.
Front row L to R: Jack Whittaker, Jack Gawthorpe,
Bill Davison, Bert Jackson, Tom Amesbury.

Parkside Artisans' Cricket Team c.1931 (Macclesfield Works Knockout Competition)
Back row L to R: Mr Butler (Head Attendant), Jack Scragg, Harold Hodgkinson,
                 Phillip Butler, -----, Albert Manssuer, Syd Barber.
Front row L to R: Ben Willock, George Nixon, Harry Horton (county cricketer),
                 Len Kellet, Harry Buckley.

Parkside Cricket Team, late 1940s.

Single Mans Football Team 1940s
Back row L to R: W Firth, Arthur Shatwell, John Crossley, J Lewis. Herbert Tomkinson, ----,
Front row L to R: Gordon Pinfield, ----, Pongo Waring, Frank Wood, Glen Batten.

Pakside Football Team 1945-46
(L to R;)   F Ashley, ----, Jack Whittaker, Trevor Whittaker, Phil Butler, George Nixon.
Standing;   J Gawthrope, B Jackson, Syd Watmough (Fire Captain)
Sitting;   Bert Ruffles, Jack Burgess, Bill Davison, Tom Amesbury, Albert Wright

Parkside Football Team 1946/47
Winners of the Macclesfield Wednesdays Workshops Knockout Competition
Standing;   J Brown, J Worthington, J Burgess, E Hodgkinson, G Pinfield, E Cockayne, J Lewis, F Ashley
Seated;   S Watmough, ----, H Ruffles, W Davison (Captain), W Firth, T Amesbury, L Lord.

Parkside Players outside Male 1 c1935, following a performance
of "HMS Pinafore".

Parkside Players in the production of "Trial By Jury" c1938. The staff orchestra in the foreground is conducted by Mr Butler.

Parkside Players in 1948, staging a performance in the Main Hall

The Main Hall ready for the staff children's party, 1948

The Main Hall prepared for the Staff dance, January 1948

Harvest festival in the Main Hall c1920s.

1947. The main hall prepared for the staff children's party, with "Snow White and the Seven Dwarfs".

Peradventure in the future,
  When I'm long since dead and gone,
And my name has been forgotten,
  Or unheard of, it's as one.
Right throughout this institution,
  One large brotherhood there'll be.
Kindred spirits, working partners,
  In a true community.
Smoother, much, life's stream will flow,
  Class and clique long dead have been.
In their place reigns selflessness,
  Outline of Utopia's seen.
Distance may be the store, wherefrom,
  The view enchantment borrows.
Effort *is* the seed ensuring
  All the new to-morrows.

Sit not back, the while thy brother
  Labours long, with might and main.
Or while the golden hours away,
  Afraid lest toil thy pride should stain.
Cast thy coat and bend thy back,
  Apply thyself with all thy will,
Inspiring others by thine efforts,
  For the summit's worth the hill.
Ample opportunity
  Offers brother, use it well,
Look but to the goal before thee,
  Far or near, none can foretell.

Courage in thine own convictions,
  Tolerance of thy brother's view.
Life is more than thee, brother,
  To it then thy pledge renew.
Unswerving fealty to thy conscience.
  Mercy with thy judgments blend.
Bringing nearer, ever nearer,
  That day when each shall call each friend.

Below: Early 1960s Parkside Players production "The Poltergeist"

Poem by Leslie Leighton, former Night Superintendent, late 1940s.

Pantomime, 1960

"Friends of Parkside" carnival float. "The friends" have given immense support
to Parkside over the years, by holding numerous events in order to raise funds
for patients' comforts.

CHAPTER 8
Medical Superintendents

Dr Peter Maury Deas (MB, MS Lond. LRCS Edin)

The first Medical Superintendent to be appointed at Parkside was Dr Peter Maury Deas (MB MS Lond. LRCS Edin), from the Royal Edinburgh Asylum for the Insane, Scotland, also known as Morningside Asylum. He became a Licentiate of the Royal College of Surgeons, Edinburgh, in 1863, then going on to study at the University of London, obtaining with honours the degree of Bachelor of Medicine in 1865 and Master of Surgery in 1866. Throughout this time he was awarded several scholarships and medals, and at one stage studied abroad. Prior to his appointment at Parkside he worked for eighteen months as Senior Assistant Physician in the Royal Edinburgh Asylum, the largest in Scotland with over 700 patients. He had also worked at two other newly opened asylums in the British Isles for a short spell, initiating their setting up, and visited several others in England and Scotland studying their management. Before devoting himself to the study of mental illness he filled successively the posts of Demonstrator of Anatomy of the College of Surgeons in Edinburgh and of Resident Surgeon at the Royal Infirmary.

There were 49 applicants for the post of Medical Superintendent; these were further reduced to a short list of 29. Testimonials in favour of Dr Deas amounted to 35, 22 of which were from some of the most eminent physicians of the time, plus a further 13 from various other scholars. One of Dr Deas' testimonials was from Sir James Young Simpson, Bart, MD, DCL Oxon, FRSE, FRCPE, a pioneer in the use of anaesthetics in 1847 when he first used chloroform to perform a surgical operation. Simpson later became Professor of Midwifery in the University of Edinburgh at the age of 29. Dr Deas applied for the post on 5th April 1869 and was later successful, taking up residence in the Medical Superintendent's house in September 1870, nine months before the completion of the hospital; at the time of his appointment he was 27 years of age. His house was furnished by Blythe and Sons. His starting salary was £350 per annum with house, coal, gas and use of garden; the number of patients in his care to be 530. A coachhouse and stable were part of the house and in later years a conservatory was added. A comparison of the same post at other County Asylums is given below:

Cheshire County Asylum (Parkside)	Salary £350 per annum with house, coal, gas and garden. Number of patients 530.
Stafford County Asylum -	Salary £500 per annum. Number of patients 500.
Derby County Asylum -	Salary £600 per annum. Number of patients 320.
Denby Asylum, North Wales -	Salary £350 per annum with house, coal and vegetables.
Prestwich Asylum -	Salary £750 per annum with house, coal and gas.

During his time as Superintendent, Dr Deas was responsible for the initial interior furnishing and decor of the main building. He worked closely with members of the Committee of Visitors and also with Robert Griffiths, the designer and architect of the main building. The general rules for the government and management of the Asylum were drawn up in 1871 and remained the same, with some slight amendments, up to 1886. Prior to the opening of the hospital on 8th May 1871, Dr Deas submitted his requirements to the Committee for 80 officers, attendants and servants to staff the hospital. On 4th April 1871 he visited the Upton Asylum at Chester to make arrangements for the first group of patients to be transferred to Parkside.

During 1872, Dr Deas initiated many new activities in the way of sports, drama and other recreational pursuits. Evening parties were organised throughout the winter with dancing, singing, Christmas carol concerts and conjuring performances. Other amusements included bagatelle, dominoes, draughts and card games. Four dance balls were held in the main hall over a twelve month period, along with four drama productions. A harmonium was purchased and requests made for the general public to join the hospital choir. The large rooms on either side of the main hall were used as recreation rooms allowing the patients to socialise. A billiard table was purchased and set up in the male recreation room. The large airing court in front of the Grand Hall was grassed over and used as a bowling green and croquet pitch where both sexes could mix and participate in a variety of recreational activities. Visits were arranged to a Panorama (rotating camera) and local theatre in Macclesfield. By 1875 cricket matches had become well established on Saturday afternoons and competitions were arranged with neighbouring clubs. A staff cricket club may well have been formed at this time, but documentary evidence for this is scant.

Records indicate that throughout his Superintendency he worked hard to establish the hospital on a sure footing, with good standards and conditions. One of his last administrative duties before he left to take up a new post was to establish the constitution and regulations for the Hospital Fire Brigade which started in 1884. Great attention was paid to safety at that time. During 1876 a survey of the Main Building had been carried out by Mr Tozer, Superintendent of the Manchester Fire Brigade, and various recommendations were made and implemented regarding fire safety. Metal fire escapes running from the rear of the four 3-storeyed blocks were built. A night watchman was appointed in 1883 to patrol the outside of the Main Building four times per night and stoke the main boilers. As with the inside of the building, push buttons linked to tell tale clocks were positioned at four stations to ensure that he was doing his job. The remains of those can be found on the outside walls of the Main Building. A fire drill was also held every week and the Hospital Fire Brigade consisted of sixteen people. The original fire alarms consisted of steam buzzers but these were replaced in the early 1890s by electric bell pushes worked by batteries. Hose carts were also supplied at this time, by Mr Holland from Broken Cross. All the wards and ancillary departments had sets of four or five fire buckets filled with water, hand forced pumps charged with a chemical liquid, wooden boxes containing standpipe and hose, and fire keys in glass boxes. Iron staircases led from some of the windows in each ward into the Asylum precincts. A horse-drawn fire engine and regular brigade completed the fire arrangements.

On Wednesday 7th June 1884, Dr Deas left to take up a new appointment at Wonford House Asylum, Exeter, Devon. A huge farewell party was held in the main hall with many notable people present, and dancing and singing went on into the small hours. By all accounts he was a very popular Superintendent. An extract from the speech given by Mr Proctor, Clerk to the Asylum, on presentation to Dr Deas of a farewell gift, also refers to his wife and children.

"I should also like to refer to the many friends that your children, young as they are, have made in the wards. Their brightness and high spirits have cheered many a poor soul that stood in sad need of cheering, and they will leave amongst the patients many a friend who will miss them and who will greatly remember their little acts of kindness".

In other parts of his speech he refers frequently to the work done by Mrs Deas for the welfare of the patients. The following extract from Dr Deas' reply talks about management:

"The first principle of management is to treat the members of the staff as individuals and not as if they were mere parts of a machine of which I was the head, compelled to certain things on being told to do them."

The gift that Dr Deas received was an epergne, an ornamental stand for the centre of a table, standing 28 inches high, in the form of a palm tree, purchased from Mr Herscher, Jeweller, of Mill Street, Macclesfield.

Dr T Steele Sheldon

Following the departure of Dr Deas to take up his new post in Devon, Dr T.Steele Sheldon was appointed Medical Superintendent in May 1884. He was the son of Alderman Sheldon, an ex-Mayor of Congleton. His personality was described as that of a kind hearted man, unostentatious, and with a quiet and retiring disposition, being a keen devotee of science and literature. Photography was one of his hobbies, along with astronomy, and at one time he had his own private observatory situated in the parkland south of the Medical Superintendent's House towards Chester Road. He may possibly have researched the effects of the phases of the moon on human behaviour, but he certainly invited many of his friends to the observatory to observe the beauties of the heavens. He was married with a daughter and son.

He superintended Parkside for 27 years and throughout that time brought about many changes for the good. An indication of the way he thought, and how he viewed the treatment of people suffering from mental illness, can be gained from some of his most often quoted comments in the reports and speeches that he made. *"We must try and make this place more like a hospital and less a place of restraint"* and *"We must treat the patients as individuals and less as cases"* were two frequently repeated sentences of his. Given this kind of thinking, had today's modern medication and treatment methods been available in 1884, then the whole course of events at Parkside and indeed in other County Asylums could well have been different and led to their closure much earlier.

Some of the most notable developments in which he played a leading part include the establishment of a small pathological laboratory in 1895 in the main building, the female epileptic block in 1891 and the male epileptic block in 1903, along with the Annexe Admission/Hospital block in 1905, the Nurses' Home, East Villa, West Villa, and Uplands private patients' block. In all these developments he played a major role, working closely with Mr Harry Beswick, the County Architect, and putting forward ideas consistent with the contemporary medical opinion of the time, and indeed many of the details incorporated in the Annexe building were to be advocated 30 years later by the Board of Control. He was instrumental in initiating lectures for nurses and attendants in the 1890s, and one of his last unfulfilled ambitions before he retired was the provision of a larger laboratory and institute at Parkside for the study of brain disease.

Another important area in which he made a worthy contribution was the provision of Sunday evening promenade concerts in the bandstand to the south side of the female wards near the Medical Superintendent's house. He also initiated the first telephone system at Parkside in 1888 when the Lancashire and Cheshire Telephonic Exchange Company Ltd provided the hospital with its first telephonic communication system between different parts of the Main Building, seven stations being installed. The rent for this came to £17 for five years. Earlier the committee had attempted to install their own system but the legal restrictions of that time prevented them from doing this.

Perhaps one of his least popular decisions was his recommendation to the Committee that the hospital brewery be closed down. This was situated in the artisans yard and was used latterly as the painter's shop. Beer had been brewed at the hospital since 1871, both for the patients and staff, but following Dr Sheldon's recommendation it closed in 1888. The following extract from Dr Sheldon's report of that year to the Committee is of interest and denotes the reasoning behind the decision to close the brewery:

"In March I submitted to your Committee a memorandum advocating the disuse of beer as an article of diet in the Asylum and it was resolved to withdraw beer for three months, to make certain alterations in the dietary and to consider the result, and in September it was resolved to make the experiment continuous. My arguments, briefly, were that alcohol is unnecessary in ordinary diet; that many lunatics are far better without it, even when it takes the form of Asylum beer; that directly or indirectly it plays a most important part in the causation of insanity; that in my opinion an attack of insanity often leaves an individual specially susceptible to its influence; and that, therefore, so practical an opportunity as is afforded by Asylum discipline of preaching the advisability of abstinence from alcohol on the part of those with unstable brains should not be lost. I then pointed out that these considerations appeared to me to outweigh the objection that, in depriving the lunatic beer, one took from him a valued portion of his diet. As an attempt at compensation (seeing that the staff were at the same time offered beer money) I suggested that changes should be made in the dietary. After eight months experience of the measure I am able to report that complaints have been remarkably few, and that the general health of the patients has not deteriorated; the diet, compared with that in other asylums, is generous and, whilst water has been substituted for beer at dinner time, tea, coffee and milk are freely given to workers and invalids."

Coffee had been given with breakfast and tea with the evening meal since the inception of the hospital. On completion of 25 years service by Dr Sheldon in December 1909 there were 1,053 patients on the register:

	Male	**Female**	**TOTAL**
East Cheshire Unions	478	522	1000
Other	4	0	4
County of Chester	1	1	2
Private and Criminal	3	3	6
TOTALS	510	543	1053

The death rate during those days was still high and in 1908 there were 88 deaths, mainly due to infectious diseases. Two of these deaths were due to a mysterious form of diarrhoea, and in September the famous Lister Institute carried out an elaborate investigation throughout the hospital, the results of which indicated that a proportion of patients were carrying typhoid bacillus. Dr Sheldon resigned, due to ill health, on 31st July 1911, after completing 27 years service as Medical Superintendent. He died in 1953.

Dr J C McConaghey, MD (Edin)

Dr McConaghey was appointed Medical Superintendent on 1st August 1911. He had previously been Second Assistant Medical Officer for ten years, with responsibility for the Annexe. He was involved in drawing up the New General Rules for the government of the hospital following the recommendations of the Commissioners in Lunacy. Like his predecessor Dr Sheldon, he was interested in research. Much interest was being generated at that time into the scientific research of mental disorders and the County of Cardiff Asylum was one of the first mental hospitals to approach the Commissioners in Lunacy with a view to obtaining state grants in order to carry out research.

Dr McConaghey was also involved with the opening of Uplands on 22nd May 1912, but unfortunately he had to resign in October 1914 due to serious illness. He died on 15th December 1937.

Dr Harry Dove Cormac, MB, MS (Madras), DPM (Manch)

Dr Cormac was appointed Medical Superintendent at the end of 1914 from a list of forty applicants, having originally been appointed to the hospital on 16th December 1905. He was to become the longest serving Medical Superintendent at Parkside, amassing a total of 32 years service, playing a leading part in the modernisation and development of the hospital at that time. It was during his superintendency that a close link was formed with Manchester University and he later became Lecturer in Mental Diseases and subsequently was appointed a Member of the Board of the Faculty of Medicine at the University.

Dr Cormac was to steer the hospital through two World Wars, in between which he provided the impetus and leadership for numerous research studies and improved training for doctors and nurses which was to benefit the whole of the patient population. At that time the medical staffing structure was different to what it is today and the Superintendent's post was a key post with much responsibility, influence and power. Consultant posts did not exist until the late 1940s and early 50s. Many of the doctors who studied at Parkside took further examinations at Manchester University and they became well versed in mental illness and neurological disorders and diseases. In 1948 Dr Young relinquished his post as Deputy Medical Superintendent to become a part time Consultant and Dr J Littlewood became Deputy Medical Superintendent.

The patient population continued to increase during Dr Cormac's term of office, with numerous extensions and additions taking place between 1918 and 1947 and it was not until the 1950s, when the deluge of pharmacological preparations came in, that the long stay patient population started to decline and the length of treatment required for new admissions became much reduced. Unfortunately, the benefits of this were not immediately obvious at the time because, following the formation of the National Health Service during 1948, the catchment area for Parkside was greatly increased, even though it had ceased to function as the County Mental Hospital.

Dr Cormac retired in 1947 and later died in 1953, just at the time that the pharmacological methods of treatment were to bring about the next era in the treatment of the mentally ill.

Dr Phillip Michael Crowe, MB, Chb (Manch), DPM (Lond)

Dr Crowe was appointed Medical Superintendent in August 1947, having started at the Hospital on 1st August 1931. He was to carry on the tradition of his predecessors, making numerous improvements and slowly getting the hospital back on its feet following the Second World War. He took on the post of Lecturer in Mental Science at Manchester University, following the retirement of Dr Cormac, having previously been Assistant Lecturer, and he was to carry on training doctors at Parkside for the Diploma in Psychological Medicine.

During the early 1950s Dr Crowe instituted a 'Bed Bureau' at the request of the Regional Board, due to gross overcrowding. In 1943 the catchment area for Parkside had been increased to include the Crewe and Nantwich area, formerly belonging to Upton Mental Hospital, Chester, which had started to become overcrowded again. The six 44-bed Villas, which had opened in 1941, were built to partly address this problem, with four of them to be used for patients from Upton who had been originally referred from the Crewe and Nantwich areas. Following regionalisation under the National Health Service Act of 1948, the catchment areas were further increased to include the north west of Derbyshire (Buxton, Chapel-en-le-Frith, Glossop, New Mills and Whaley Bridge), plus that part of the Borough of Stockport which formerly lay in the County of Lancashire, and Lancashire No 17 Area (Audenshaw, Droylsden, Denton and Mossley). The net result of this was that, whereas the annual admission rate at that time was 200, by 1951 this had risen to 400 annually for the previous three years. In order to relieve this problem, full use was made of the hospital beds at Lake Hospital in Ashton-under-Lyne, Shaw Heath Hospital in Stockport, Barony Hospital in Nantwich, and Ollerset View in New Mills. This was probably to be one of Dr Crowe's most onerous and difficult administrative tasks, and it was not until the start of the 1960s that overcrowding began to resolve itself, as a result of new methods of treatment rather than reorganising the catchment areas.

Dr P.M.Crowe was followed by Dr R.Boardman who took a keen interest in electro-encephalography, by which time the EEG Department had become well established, and it still provides an excellent service today with the EEG tracings expertly read by Dr M.S.Bethell.

Following Dr R.Boardman's departure to a post abroad, Dr J.Littlewood took over, having previously started as Third Medical Assistant during the early thirties. On 16th May 1942 he joined Her Majesty's Forces in the Royal Army Medical Corps. He returned to the hospital in June 1947 to give many years of devoted service, and was to become the last serving Medical Superintendent at Parkside, retiring in the early 1970s.

Eventually, Consultant posts became established and a new method of medical administration began, known as the 'Cogwheel system', in which each Consultant took it in turns to attend to medical administrative matters. Since then numerous administrative changes have occurred and at present we have the new development of the two tier purchaser/provider system.

Parkside Fire Brigade early 1930s

Back row L to R: Jack Thompson, Bill Davison, Sid Holden, Ted Proctor,
Len Beech, Alec Stubbs, Ralph Lonsdale.

Front row L to R: George Davies, Tom Amesbury, Harold Dean (Assistant Engineer
and Fire Captain), Ernie Cockayne.

Willys Knight saloon
c.1929, similar to the car
originally belonging to
Dr Cormac, which was
converted into a fire
engine at the beginning
of the Second World War
(see picture next page)

Fire Drill competition.

Parkside Hospital Fire Brigade before the days of the fire engine. Dr Deas initiated the Fire Brigade in 1883.

Parkside Fire Brigade early 1940s
Back row L to R: Syd Barber, Stan Livingstone, Wilfred Silman, Ted Proctor, George Watts, Ben Willock.
Front row L to R: Len Kellett, George Nixon, Sid Watmough, Fred Moss, Les Willock.

Dr T Steele Sheldon,
Second Medical Superintendent 1884-1911

From Sir James Y. Simpson, Bart., M.D., D.C.L. Oxon., F.R.S.E., F.R.C.P.E., *Professor of Midwifery in the University of Edinburgh ; Physician-Accoucheur to the Queen in Scotland ; one of the Medical Board of the Royal Edinburgh Asylum.*

52 Queen Street,
Edinburgh, *November* 18, 1868.

I HAVE much pleasure in stating that I remember Dr. P. M. Deas as one of the most distinguished students of his time in our University.

The high honours he carried off at the Examinations of the London University, the able manner in which he discharged the duties of Demonstrator at the College of Surgeons, and his fluency as a debater at the Medical Societies, made him well known to, and respected by, his teachers and fellow-students.

He has for some years devoted himself to the study of psychology, and in the large Asylum at Morningside must have had sufficient experience to render him eminently fit for the post he is applying for.

J. Y. SIMPSON.

Dr Deas' 1868 testimonial from
Sir James Young Simpson

Opening of the Staff Social Club.
From centre L to R; Mr Patterson,
Mr Solly, Dr Littlewood
(last medical Superintendent at Parkside. At the end of January 1997, Parkside Hospital closed and on the 1st February Dr J.Littlewood died aged 89. He gave the Hospital over 40 years of loyal and unstinting service from1934 and was the seventh and last Medical Superintendent).

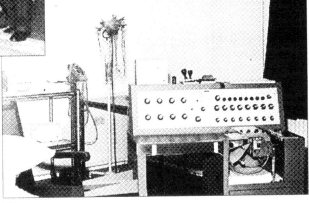

1950 Early EEG Machine, one of only two in the country at that time.

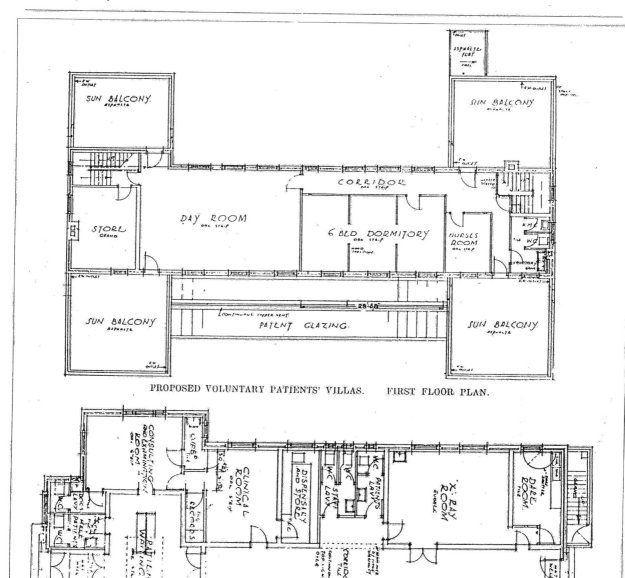

PROPOSED VOLUNTARY PATIENTS' VILLAS. FIRST FLOOR PLAN.

PROPOSED OUT-PATIENTS' CLINIC.
GROUND FLOOR PLAN.

Plan of Rosemount Out Patients Department 1939.

CHAPTER 9
Rosemount Out Patients Complex

The first semblance of an Out Patients Department at Parkside began in 1935 in a room next to Male 3 Ward in the main building. It was following the Mental Treatment Act of 1930 that people first mooted the idea of out patient treatment as an alternative to admission. During 1935 a total of 45 new patients were seen, with the total attendance of new and old patients being 145. Of the 45 new patients who attended in 1935, 41 were referred by their own private doctors, and four attended on their own without any introductory letter. Ten were treated at the clinic, six had a report done on them and were then referred back to their private doctors, relatives or other authority. Nineteen were admitted on a temporary basis. By 1942, the last year of the Out Patients Clinic in the main building, 55 patients were treated and the total number of attendances had increased to 375, with the average attendance per session at 3.6.

Rosemount Clinic opened in 1943 along with two detached early treatment Villas. The Clinic itself is a detached flat-roofed 1930s style building, situated to the south east boundary of the estate beyond Uplands. The complex of three buildings is approached by its own drive off Chester Road so that its connection with the main hospital is not obvious. During the Second World War, the two Villas were used as nursing quarters by nurses from the Annexe Emergency Medical Hospital run by the military.

One Villa was built for female patients and the other for males, each with a capacity of 18 beds. At the time of opening, the ground floor of each Villa consisted of a verandah facing south with a floor of pressed stone flags, a dining room, day room, kitchen, nurses' room, duty room, toilet and wash area. The room on the extreme left of the building, looking towards it from Chester Road, was a six-bedded dormitory. A corridor and six single side rooms with a bed in each, opening out with French windows onto the south facing verandah, completed this not unattractive building. The first floor consisted of a six-bedded dormitory, a large day room, store, nurses' room, toilets and wash room. Four sun lounges on each corner of the building completed the arrangement.

The Out Patients Clinic is central to the two Villas facing south, gained via a drive from Chester Road. The usage of the rooms in the clinic has changed over the years, but originally, on entering from the Chester Road end, there was the waiting room, to the right of which was the Social Worker's Office, and to the left the Consulting and Examination Room. The film cupboard was also on the right, and medical records room to the left.

Double doors led into a long corridor with five separate rooms on each side. On the right hand side was the staff room, hydrotherapy room with two baths, patients' dressing room, massage and electro-therapy room, and at the far end the actinotherapy room (a form of light treatment). The left hand side consisted of clinical room, dispensary and store, lavatories, X-ray room panelled with rubber and dark room.

In later years other treatments were carried out, including modified electro-convulsion treatment, and for many years an ear, nose and throat clinic was operated. Every student nurse had their ears tested on the audiometer. Psychiatric Social Workers were seconded from Manchester University and did part of their training at Rosemount.

The opening of the clinic marked a significant advance forward in the treatment of mental illness and it became highly successful, largely through the efforts of Dr Cormac, the Medical Superintendent, ably assisted by Dr Crowe and Dr Aitken. Dr Crowe even held an evening clinic for people unable to attend during the day because of work commitments.

The following extract from the Medical Superintendent's report for 1945 amply demonstrates the progressive nature of the hospital at that time:

"In the joint proposals made by the Royal Medico-Psychological Association, the Royal College of Physicians and the British Medical Association as to the treatment of mental illness, it is recommended that a special out patient and early treatment centre should be provided at every mental hospital. It may be of interest to note that Parkside is the only mental hospital in the country that has already made this provision.

The need for this centre is shown by the fact that 161 patients attended the clinic during the year on 941 occasions. Of this number 139 were new cases. The marked success of this department is due to the excellent work of my colleague, Dr Crowe, and Dr Aitken who assists him".

From this beginning other out patient clinics were to follow, based in outlying areas, thus saving the need for people to travel long distances. Dr R.M.Young opened clinics at Stockport and Ashton-under-Lyne, and later still clinics opened at Congleton and Knutsford. More Social Worker posts were created and in 1955 Mrs Rastall became the first Clinical Psychologist to be appointed at Parkside.

By 1955 the total number of patients attending the clinic was 820, with 566 new patients, 4,795 attendances, and an average number of weekly sessions of 11.

Over the years the work of Rosemount Clinic has continued to grow and it remains an important part of the community treatment requirement. A depot clinic has been established along with a lithium clinic. The Villa to the right of the clinic from the Chester Road end is now used as the Pennine Day Hospital and the Villa to the left as the Alcohol Treatment Unit, although the long term future of this complex remains in doubt.

Rosemount Out Patients Clinic opened in 1943, with Early Treatment Villas behind.

CHAPTER 10
In Summary

The county asylum movement evolved within the setting of the workhouse and private madhouse systems. The 1774 Act brought about the establishment of a system of inspection for all madhouses and asylums. This originally consisted of five commissioners from the College of Physicians who had the power to grant licenses or take them away; no person was to keep more than one lunatic in his/her house without a license. Boarding out arrangements for mentally ill people were quite common at that time.

The 1828 Act replaced the five commissioners with 15 Metropolitan Commissioners and the 1843 Act increased those to 20. Following the 1845 Act the Commissioners in Lunacy became a central inspecting body for all asylums in England and Wales with the exception of Bethlem Hospital. The commissioners pursued inspections with vigour and were responsible for many changes and improvements in county asylums particularly after the 1845 Act.

Many private madhouses and asylums before the 19th century produced outstanding philanthropists, neurologists and psychologists who devoted much of their time to the study and treatment of the mentally ill. The county asylums carried on this tradition well into the 20th century with numerous physicians and medical superintendents striving for new treatments, ideas and a more humanistic approach.

Workhouses housed a large number of mentally ill people and when they were transferred to the purpose built, relatively comfortable, conditions of the new county asylums this fuelled a period of therapeutic optimism discussed in earlier chapters. The madhouse system arose during the mid-seventeenth century, reaching its heyday during the last quarter of the eighteenth and early part of the nineteenth century when the county asylum movement gradually caused its downfall. By 1848, one half of all mentally ill people in asylums throughout England and Wales were in private licensed houses. Many of these took in pauper lunatics in addition to the poorer classes of paying patients, middle and upper classes. By the mid 18th century medical men had started to take the interests of the mentally ill in hand and were increasingly appointed to manage private madhouses. Advertisements to treat patients in domestic settings became more common. Many clients lived in cottages in the grounds of the larger establishments. Performance targets were set for staff and some houses promoted themselves with a 'no cure-no pay' policy and plenty of statistical information for intending purchasers of their services

Unfortunately the private madhouse system attracted a large number of proprietors who exploited the system for financial gain thus influencing public opinion and ultimately bringing the system into disrepute. This became known at the time as the 'Trade in Lunacy'. In addition it also lacked any form of corporate identity, properties tended to be scattered and inspections were infrequent and very often inadequate. They remained isolated from the contemporary, mainstream developments which had started to take place in the new county asylums, especially with regard to training attendants, nursing and medical staff. In 1841 the inaugural meeting of the Medico-Psychological Association took place at Gloucester Lunatic Asylum. This became the main professional body to which all reputable medical and nursing staff belonged and in 1925 was granted a Royal Charter. It continued to conduct nursing examinations until 1950. The amount of good work and professionalism generated by this organisation is beyond doubt, being well documented in its own 'Journal of Mental Science'. The new asylums saw the arrival of medical superintendents pursuing the latest medical developments and treatments; the proprietors of madhouses had tended to be lay people.

On average most private madhouses accommodated around twenty clients but there were also houses with small groups of around two to four clients. Only a small number of houses were purpose built, the majority being purchased and refurbished and similar architecturally to many of today's group home properties. Indeed the current mental nursing homes and small group houses are a direct descendant of the private madhouses of the seventeenth and eighteenth centuries. We tend to think that care in the community is a recent concept, but as with so many other developments history proves us wrong.

The disparaging and sometimes exaggerated criticisms levelled at private madhouses were not altogether justifiable. There were many responsible proprietors who ran good houses, displaying humane, charitable and progressive attitudes. Some houses had well defined aims, objectives and treatment plans of six to twelve weeks, whereupon the clients would be discharged home or to other accommodation. The good reputation of the better licensed houses depended on enlightened, caring and progressive treatments as opposed to mere custodial methods.

However, private licensed madhouses continued to be viewed with suspicion for over two centuries because of the conflict between duty and pecuniary gain. Owning a madhouse could be a lucrative business which very often ran in the family. Competition for contracts between houses tended to keep costs as low as possible.

Only one or two studies of private licensed madhouses have been carried out. These looked at metropolitan houses, largely ignoring the provincial houses, with one or two exceptions. Despite the asylum movement many reputable madhouses continued well into the 20th century. The name was unfortunate, but under the Public Health Act 1936 they became known as Mental Nursing Homes. Much historical research is required in order to obtain a clearer picture and better evaluation of this important period in the history of psychiatry. Successive writers have tended to repeat the disparaging view of the madhouses in the absence of any detailed research.

Most of the county asylums in the British Isles were mainly built during the Victorian era, particularly from the mid 19th century through to the early part of the 20th century. They were built with great care; neglect and ill treatment became less. Further measures to curb ill treatment, and the business-like culture in the private madhouses came about following the Lunacy Act of 1890. It prohibited the enlargement of private licensed houses or only under exceptional circumstances. The concept of catchment areas came into being with the county asylum movement; private madhouses did not have catchment areas. Some authorities were slow to comply with their duty to build asylums, mainly for financial reasons. Norwich Corporation evaded their duty and eventually legal proceedings were taken against them by the Secretary of State. Similar social and architectural parallels took place in Europe and America. In France one asylum, by the mid 18th century, housed 7,800 patients and in America 32 state asylums were built between 1841 and 1887. Connoly's approach was largely used in America but on the continent Pinel and Esquirol influenced developments along with others, as with the English asylums.

Likewise the majority of general hospitals, including Infirmaries, Isolation Hospitals and other specialist hospitals were built between 1860 and the First World War. Community Cottage hospitals continued to be built up to 1939 at an average of one every seven weeks from 1859.

Towards the end of the 19th century workers in the mental health field had started to evolve a system of classification based on clinical pictures which is still in use today. Charcot, Janet and Freud became the pioneers of the psychological classification, whilst Warnike, Kraeplin and later Bleuler centred on the localisation of cerebral function. Kretschmer retained the somatological approach. Between them, and along with other notable workers, a better system of classification was established and probably led to the largely eclectic approach which is still in use.

The idea to close down the large county mental hospitals by the year 2000 was conceived in 1961, when the benefits of newer methods of treatment had already started to become apparent. In a passionate speech, the then Minister of Health, Enoch Powell, described the large mental hospitals, *'There they stand isolated, majestic, imperious, brooded over by the great water tower and chimney combined, rising unmistakable and daunting out of the countryside.'*

The actual closures did not start to take place until much later, particularly after 1980 when further health service reforms were being planned. By March 1993, thirty eight of the largest mental hospitals had closed, the number of beds dropping to 28,000 from 140,000 in 1960. A further nine had closed by January 1996, thus bringing the total to forty seven with forty one more due to be sold off by the end of the century. The scale of these closures is now being compared by some writers with the dissolution of the monasteries.

The biggest changes, as a result of the above closures, have been in the type of accommodation, level of supervision, quantity and quality of care given to the mentally ill. From 1982 to 1992 the number of beds in the large mental hospitals fell from 68,555 to less than 28,500. The number of psychiatric beds in district general and cottage hospitals rose slightly from 15,145 to 21,830 and Local Authority nursing homes increased their accommodation for the mentally ill from 4,173 to 7,552 beds. During this time beds for the elderly were reclassified as 'Elderly mentally infirm'. The biggest expansion has occurred in the voluntary and private sector. Voluntary residential places rose from 1,603 in 1982 to 4,303 in 1992 and private places 1,994 to 12,653. (Figures taken from the Department of Health study carried out by researchers at Birmingham Universities Health Services Management Centre.)

Good Intentions in Fine Surroundings

The Parkside estate continued to grow over the years. The acquisition of more land on which to build new units and extensions to existing buildings; the expansion of the hospital farm and areas of market gardens were all designed for the needs of a growing hospital population. All these developments were well-intentioned with the best interests of the patients in mind. Those patients who at that time were thought of as untreatable, were never lost sight of in the plan, and remained central to it. It was for their benefit that a suitable environment was created in which they could lead as near a normal life as possible. At the same time some of these developments were fuelled by a growing realisation that mental illness was treatable and it was for this reason that the Annexe and all subsequent developments were built. The Annexe was designed so that better care, understanding, diagnosis and treatment could be carried out. Again it must not be forgotten that treatments for a wide variety of physical diseases and disorders had yet to be discovered and that the pharmaceutical industry was still in its infancy.

By the end of Queen Victoria's reign in 1901, the number of beds at Parkside stood at 798. Contrary to popular belief over 50% of Parkside was built after the Victorian era with a total of 802 beds added by 1950, thus bringing the total to 1600.

Beautiful Parkland

Also at this time the hospital parkland was developing. In later years some considered it the fourth park of Macclesfield, along with its wide range of sports pitches. The grounds contain some good specimens of trees, planted singly or in groups. The more noteworthy ones include the Weymouth or White Pine (Pinus strobus), a North American species with the ability to thrive in exposed situations. It became known as the Weymouth Pine in England when it was planted extensively by Lord Weymouth at Longleat, Wiltshire, some 200 years ago. Another pine to be found is the Corsican or Black Pine (Pinus nigra), with its handsome trunk and pleasing bark, a native of southern Italy, Corsica and Sicily. Other coniferous species to be seen in the grounds include varieties of Chamaecyparis, Abies, Cedrus and Taxus.

A good selection of deciduous trees are also to be found, including Common Beech (Fagus sylvatica) along with its copper form. One of the most interesting trees in the grounds is the Fern-Leaved Beech (Fagus sylvatica var lacinata) with its narrowly pointed deep cut leaves. This is a most handsome tree and a fine mature specimen is to be found growing in the grassed area near the Works Department. It usually bears a good crop of mast each year. In the Annexe area are to be seen good specimens of Weeping Ash (Fraxinus excelsoir var Pendula) with branches sweeping down to ground level.

Many other deciduous trees can be seen throughout the parkland including varieties of Oak, Maple, Lime and Chestnut. A particularly fine specimen of the Horse Chestnut (Aesculus hippocastanum) is to be found growing near the old Self Care Unit. A good avenue of pleached Limes is to be seen on each side of the driveway leading to Uplands and along the perimeter of the former tennis courts.

Over the years the parkland has always provided an abundance of wildlife. Breeding pairs of Badgers and Foxes could be found, along with the ubiquitous Grey Squirrel which was first introduced into this country during the late 19th century at nearby Henbury Park by the Brocklehurst family. Many species of birds have been seen in the parkland. A patient who lived happily in the hospital for over twenty years, who was a member of the Royal Society for the Protection of Birds and the British Trust for Ornithology, kept a record of all the species he had seen in the grounds. This included a good cross section of British birds along with some rarities. The author, as recently as summer 1995, noted two breeding pairs of Spotted Flycatchers. Regular residents and visitors have included Nuthatch, Treecreeper, Tawny Owl, Goldfinch, Waxwing, Warblers and many others.

A Centre of Excellence

Following the building of the Annexe much enthusiasm was generated and it became 'the place to be' or, in modern parlance, a 'centre of excellence'. A wide variety of treatments, research and surveys were carried out in the Annexe. Lecture rooms, a Nurse training school and numerous treatment rooms came about. Knowledge was shared and many of the leading medical people of the time visited the Annexe, giving lectures and demonstrating and participating in research programmes. A close link was formed with Manchester Royal Hospital and the Medical Superintendent at that time, Dr H.D.Cormac, was appointed to the Faculty of Medicine at the University; many of his contemporaries were the key medical people of the time.

The Manchester Medical School had grown rapidly towards the end of the Victorian era and in 1894 the Faculty Buildings were enlarged and became a University Faculty. Slowly along with Manchester Royal Infirmary a local tradition in neurology was established and in 1883 Manchester University offered its own Medical degree. Originally Doctors took Scottish degrees, this was later followed after 1860 by London degrees.

This tradition in neurology was maintained during the Edwardian period and many competent local medical men emerged, some of whom were Dr H.D.Cormac's contemporaries including the Edwardian anatomist Grafton Elliot Smith along with Professor J.S.B.Stopford who lectured frequently at Parkside. In later years he was instrumental, with several others, in planning for the formation of the Manchester Regional Health Board of which he was to become the first Chairman following the initiative of the National Health Service in 1948.

The Royal Medico Psychological Association held many meetings in the Annexe on a regular basis providing a platform for the exchange of ideas. Much research was done by the medical and nursing representatives and further knowledge fostered.

The Parkside laboratory carried out an enormous amount of work over the years which contributed greatly to a better understanding of the nature of infection, physiological disorders and dietary needs. Post mortem examinations were carried out in Parkside's own mortuary with meticulous examination notes being kept for survey and research purposes.

Many of the medical staff went abroad to study and gain further knowledge and experience; always returning to the hospital to share their new ideas with enthusiasm.

The areas of beautiful grounds and parkland which accompanied the large county asylums were one of there greatest assets on a par with the large country mansion. At that time the motor car was not widespread and many asylums were built near railway stations to allow easy access for visitors.

Annual sports days held in the grounds along with fancy dress balls and musical entertainments in the main and Annexe halls, attracted crowds of ordinary people. The Grand Halls were used for concerts, courses, dances and other cultural activities and combined with the sports grounds and swimming pools one could perhaps compare them favourably with modern day leisure centres. Chapels, follies, pavilions and elevated views were common features when asylums were originally built but of course over the years many of those wonderful views have been obliterated by further developments.

When many of the country's hospitals were built, the planners could not have foreseen the huge growth in the use of the private motor car or envisaged the widespread air, noise and environmental pollution which is now presenting as a serious health problem. As inner city and town hospitals gradually become enveloped by high density developments, car parks, roundabouts and roads, we may well see a return to new health units and clinics being built out in the countryside, where the air is fresher and the surroundings more aesthetically pleasing.

With modern health care systems now driven by market forces there is no doubt that smaller health units, nursing homes, clinics and maybe some hospitals will get larger, with add-on fashionable developments and lucrative diagnostic and treatment facilities. Already we hear of extensions to existing properties such as nursing homes, group homes and clinics. Some have added occupational therapy departments, swimming pools and gymnasiums, others have been purpose built out in the countryside and lavishly advertised as new concerns. This begs the question of how far we really have come along the road in terms of the social and architectural development of health care buildings.

Currently we have a mix of health and social care as the funding for the mentally ill, the elderly and those with learning disabilities slowly moves from free health needs to means tested social ones. Trying to decide who qualifies for which can be a tricky business and increasing numbers of people end up being shunted between the two. The main players influencing developments at the moment are the new wave of health service business managers; whilst the authority of the doctors has been slowly emasculated. This change in managerial style has always been with us throughout history. The churches, monasteries, a variety of charitable institutions played a huge part in the care of the mentally ill. Then came the business proprietors of the private madhouses followed by the medical people. No doubt this progression will continue. There have been outstanding models of success, and failures from all the different systems. Perhaps the most consistent feature is how each succeeding generation always seems to think its ideas, concepts and systems are better than those of the preceding generations.

The philanthropy of the Victorians produced many magnificent mental hospitals on sites of outstanding natural beauty. Whilst some retain this beauty others have lost it in subsequent add on developments of modern times. A conservation battle is now being waged over the future of former workhouses, general hospitals and psychiatric hospitals. Over 2000 of these are judged to be of historic interest and some 600 are listed. As health authorities sell off their land and hospitals to developers in accordance with government directives, many end up being demolished and replaced by supermarkets, roads and roundabouts, their grounds lost for ever. As hospital closures gain momentum many stand in states of disrepair and become vandalised.

Happily a more enlightened attitude is starting to develop between planners and property developers as they realise the stunning potential inherent in these institutions. Some are starting to understand and appreciate Victorian values and we have recently heard of Grand Halls being restored to their former glory, together with sports facilities incorporated into a mix of the old original hospital buildings following renovation and improvements, along with new properties. In the case of some psychiatric hospitals the former patients still live on the original site in modern homes. One property developer is redeveloping an existing hospital to a 'total lifestyle village' similar to Port Sunlight and Saltaire, the well known model villages with their close knit communities and social facilities built by Victorian philanthropists. Maybe the Victorians got it right after all!

Private Madhouses circa 1890

Despite the asylum movement, many reputable private licensed madhouses continued well into the twentieth century. The name was unfortunate but the modern day mental nursing homes and group houses are the direct descendants of the madhouse system. Under the Public Health Act of 1936 they became known as Mental Nursing Homes.

SOUTH BEACON.

HADLOW DOWN, BUXTED, SUSSEX.

ESTABLISHED 1892.

Telegrams: "Hadlow Down."   *Stations:* Buxted, Mayfield or Heathfield.

40 Acres of Farm and Recreation Ground.

Driving, Motoring, Golf and all Outdoor recreations.

Treatment of Nervous or slight Mental Breakdown.

TERMS FROM 3 GUINEAS PER WEEK.

BOREATTON PARK.

Founded by the late W. H. O. SANKEY, M.D., F.R.C.P., for the reception of a limited number of ladies and gentlemen mentally afflicted, and now conducted on the same lines by his son, E. H. O. SANKEY, M.A., M B., B.C.Cantab.

THE CROFT.

A comfortable cottage residence, where one gentleman can have special care and attention without necessarily coming into contact with other patients.

If desirable he can enjoy all the recreations provided at South Beacon—Motoring, Riding, Golf.

The original cricket pavilion and a match in progress

Bowling Green and
Tennis courts enclosed
by pleached lime trees.
The Annexe can be
seen in the background

Looking east towards the Clock Tower

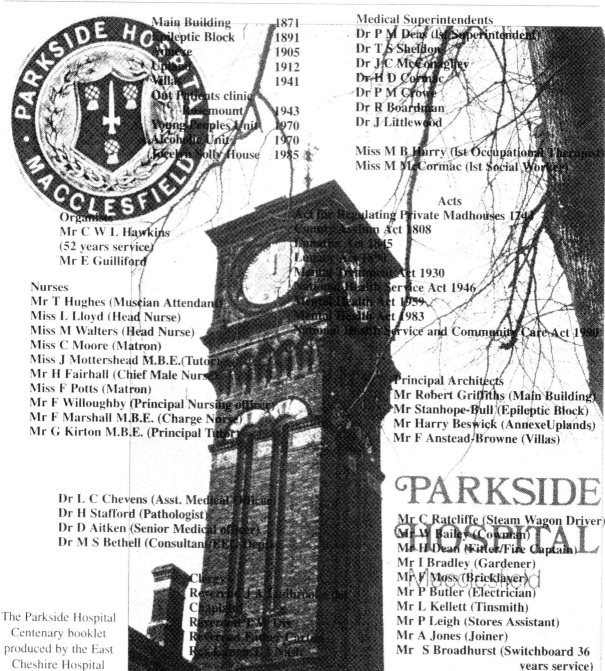

PARKSIDE HOSPITAL · MACCLESFIELD

Main Building	1871
Epileptic Block	1891
Annexe	1905
Uplands	1912
Villas	1941
Out Patients clinic	
Beaumount	1943
Young Peoples Unit	1970
Alcoholic Unit	1970
Jocelyn Solly House	1985

Medical Superintendents
Dr P M Deas (1st Superintendent)
Dr T S Sheldon
Dr J C McConaghey
Dr H D Cormac
Dr P M Crowe
Dr R Boardman
Dr J Littlewood

Miss M B Hurry (1st Occupational Therapist)
Miss M McCormac (1st Social Worker)

Organist
Mr C W L Hawkins
(52 years service)
Mr E Guilliford

Acts
Act for Regulating Private Madhouses 1774
County Asylum Act 1808
Lunatics Act 1845
Lunacy Act 1890
Mental Treatment Act 1930
National Health Service Act 1946
Mental Health Act 1959
Mental Health Act 1983
National Health Service and Community Care Act 1990

Nurses
Mr T Hughes (Muscian Attendant)
Miss L Lloyd (Head Nurse)
Miss M Walters (Head Nurse)
Miss C Moore (Matron)
Miss J Mottershead M.B.E.(Tutor)
Mr H Fairhall (Chief Male Nurse)
Miss F Potts (Matron)
Mr F Willoughby (Principal Nursing officer)
Mr F Marshall M.B.E. (Charge Nurse)
Mr G Kirton M.B.E. (Principal Tutor)

Principal Architects
Mr Robert Griffiths (Main Building)
Mr Stanhope-Bull (Epileptic Block)
Mr Harry Beswick (AnnexeUplands)
Mr F Anstead-Browne (Villas)

Dr L C Chevens (Asst. Medical Officer)
Dr H Stafford (Pathologist)
Dr D Aitken (Senior Medical officer)
Dr M S Bethell (Consultant EEG Dept.)

PARKSIDE HOSPITAL Macclesfield

Mr C Ratcliffe (Steam Wagon Driver)
Mr W Bailey (Cowman)
Mr H Dean (Fitter/Fire Captain)
Mr I Bradley (Gardener)
Mr F Moss (Bricklayer)
Mr P Butler (Electrician)
Mr L Kellett (Tinsmith)
Mr P Leigh (Stores Assistant)
Mr A Jones (Joiner)
Mr S Broadhurst (Switchboard 36 years service)

Clergy
Reverend J Goodbrook M.A.
Chaplain
Reverend E H Dix
Reverend James Caulfield
Reverend T G Nash

Colonel Antrobus (Committee Chairman)
Colonel Brocklehurst (Committee Chairman)
Mrs Cooke (Committee Chairman)
Mrs Solly (Committee Chairman)

1871 1971

The Parkside Hospital Centenary booklet produced by the East Cheshire Hospital Management Committee - along with a medley of names to remember.

Chronological Table of Principal Developments

1803 The term 'psychiatry' coined by Johan Reil

1808 County Asylum Act passed recommending separate accommodation for the mentally ill in each county, but not compulsory (**Wynn's Act**).

1811 County rate raised in order to build more asylums.

1825 Robert Griffiths born, the architect of the main building at Parkside.

1827 Nine County Asylums in England and Wales with an average of 116 patients in each.

1829 Chester Asylum built at Upton near Chester (still standing) by the architect William Cole, who also designed Bolesworth Castle.

1843 Dr P M Deas born, who later became the first Medical Superintendent at Parkside.

1845 The workhouse on Prestbury Road, Macclesfield built to designs by the architects Scott & Moffatt. Later became West Park Hospital with its own chapel.

The Lunacy Act of 1845 made the building of County Asylums compulsory.

166 Asylums recognised by law at this time in England and Wales.

17 County Asylums

11 Asylums of mixed character, i.e. maintained either by subscription or charitable income.

2 Military and Naval Asylums.

99 Houses licensed by Justices in Session.

37 Houses licensed by the Metropolitan Commissioners

The number of mentally ill people to be found in the various institutions at that time:

9,339 in Workhouses

4,400 in County Asylums

3,346 in Provincial licensed houses

1,827 in Metropolitan licensed houses

879 in other public asylums

563 in Bethlem and St.Luke's

168 in Military and Naval Hospitals

It was because twice as many mentally ill people were still confined to workhouses and elsewhere that the 1845 Act made the building of county asylums compulsory in England and Wales. At that time the Asylum with the highest cure rate was Chester with 63.2% and the lowest cure rate was Liverpool with 31.4%.

1843-48 Jeremiah Clarke rented a house called Park Side (remains recently demolished) from the Governors of Macclesfield Free Grammar School on land which was later to be built the New Cheshire County Asylum. Cheadle Royal Mental Hospital, Heald Green built to the designs of architect Richard Lane, who also designed Stockport Infirmary and the Church of St.Thomas, Henbury.

1864 Chester Asylum, Upton, becomes overcrowded.

1866 Court of Quarter Sessions meet in Chester Castle and decide to build a new County Asylum for Cheshire in Macclesfield.

1868-71 Main Building (still standing) built to the designs of Robert Griffiths, along with the Church of St.Luke (still standing), Hospital Farm (since demolished), Head Attendants Lodge on Chester Road (since demolished), Bridge Lodge on Victoria Road (still standing) for the Head Gardener, Main Entrance Lodge on Victoria Road for the engineer (still standing), and the bridge across Victoria Road from Bridge Lodge (since demolished).

25th March 1868 a contract entered into with Henry Lovatt of Wolverhampton for the excavation of the foundations.

19th October 1868 a further contract for the superstructure with the exception of the excited blocks and connecting corridor ranges and side rooms.

24th August 1870 a further contract for the construction of two excited blocks at the extreme ends of the main building along with the connecting corridors and side rooms.

Opening date 8th May 1871. 702 beds. Total cost to original design £133,835. Named the Cheshire County Asylum, Macclesfield. Final cost £141,823 3s 5d.

Dr.P.M.Deas appointed Medical Superintendent. 295 patients by the end of the first year.

Macclesfield Infirmary also built to designs by James Stevens (1867-1872) opening in 1872 with 116 beds.

1870-73 Three boreholes drilled on the Parkside site for water. The 1873 one was drilled by the Manchester firm, Mather & Platt, and became the hospital well.

1871-89 Visiting Committee of Justices supervised the hospital, appointed by the Court of Quarter Session.

1874 Part of the 1st Floor of the Female Infirmary Block converted into a ward for 24 private patients.

1884 Dr.T.S.Sheldon appointed Medical Superintendent in May (2nd Medical Superintendent).
Hospital Fire Brigade started.

1886 Water storage reservoir constructed with capacity of 248,000 gallons

1888 Death of Robert Griffiths, architect of the Main Building (County Surveyor for 25 years), on 29th May aged 63 years.
Hospital Brewery closes.

1889 Hospital taken over by the Cheshire County Council. Committee of Visitors appointed and house sub-committee (day to day running). This arrangement lasted for 58 years.

1890 583 Patients in the hospital. Nurse training begins.
Lunacy Act of 1890 sets out how asylums should be run.

1891 Female epileptic block built between the clock tower and laundry facing north (still stands). Two storeys for 96 patients at a cost of £6,756. 9s 9d. Accommodation for 10 nursing staff.
Total accommodation for patients increased to 744.

1893 Land for the proposed Annexe/Infirmary Admission Hospital purchased from the Governors of Macclesfield Free Grammar School on 26th September 1893.

1895 Small Pathological Laboratory set up in the Main Building.

1896 Isolation Hospital built (since demolished).

1898 Main sewers laid to the hospital by George Roylance, Waters Green, Macclesfield.

1902 Nurses Home built (still standing) for 32 nurses (female) near Church of St.Luke .
Mary Dendy Hospital formed at Great Warford, along with the Margaret Barclay Homes.

1903 Male epileptic block (still standing) opened in the spring, for 50 patients. Situated between the clock tower and artisans yard at the cost of £6,782 including furniture. Designed and planned by Henry Beswick, County Architect for Cheshire.

1904 Chaplain's post becomes non-resident.
The famous David Lewis Centre for Epilepsy opened at Warford (not a part of Parkside of course).

1905 Annexe/Infirmary Admission Hospital opened 19th July. Designed by Harry Beswick (County Architect) with a capacity of 220 beds. Total cost including Annexe, Female Nurses Home and Male Epileptic Block came to £80,359 11s 11d (still standing).
Patient numbers increased from 806 to 1026.
Parkside Staff Cricket Club probably formed.

1906-07 Hospital well deepened to a depth of 344 feet.

1908 Back Lane Farmhouse, (still standing) Priory Lane, converted into cottages for 8 farm working patients and a married attendant.

1909 1,053 patients on the register.

1910 By 1910, ninety one new asylums had been built in England with an average of 1,072 patients in each.
East Villa and West Villa (now demolished) opened in September between the Annexe and Victoria Road. 43 patients in each villa. Designed by Harry Beswick (County Architect) at a cost of £25,000.

1911 New set of rules for the government and management of the hospital introduced.
Dr.J.C.McConaghey appointed Medical Superintendent on 1st August (3rd Medical Superintendent).
New cricket pitch laid out east of East Villa. Original pitch near hospital church.

1912 Uplands Private Villa opened 22nd May on the high ground off Chester Road near Rosemount House. Designed and planned by Harry Beswick. (still standing)

1914   Dr.H.D.Cormac appointed Medical Superintendent in December (4th Medical Superintendent). Became the longest serving Medical Superintendent amassing a total of 32 years.

1915   Three fields, purchased on 19th February from Miss Winifred Vane Barnshaw at a cost of £100 per acre, to the west of the hospital between Chester Road and Fallibroome Road.
Total area of the estate at that time was 179 acres, 40 acres of buildings and roads, 153 acres owned by the County and 26 acres held by the committee on annual tenancy

1916   Whole of the Main Building lit by electricity. Prior to 1890 gas lighting was used.
1,317 patients now in the hospital.

1918   80 acres under the plough.
22 allotments let to staff at 1 shilling per 100 sq.yds.

1919   Two disused sewage tanks converted into water storage tanks in order to store water collected from the roof of the main building. Total capacity 60,000 gallons.

1920-21 Change of name from Cheshire County Asylum to Cheshire County Mental Hospital.
Three year course for nurse training established. Dental room provided and equipped.
Pathological laboratory fully equipped and visiting pathologist appointed. This became the main laboratory for other hospitals and GP Practices in Macclesfield District and during the Second World War assumed area status.

Further purchase of land at Upton from the Governors of Macclesfield Grammar School of 4 acres 2 roods.
Alterations, additions and improvements occurred every year from 1921-46.

1922-23 12.308 acres rented from Colonel Beck's trustees.
Refrigerator fitted in the butcher's shop. Central heating provided in main building.
Numerous treatment rooms fitted out in the Annexe.
Start of occupational therapy. Large army hut erected on cricket field 60' x 20'. 100 patients participate in a variety of activities. Relatives and friends attend.
Occupational therapy officers appointed.
Canteen for patients and staff opened.
Parole card system introduced on some wards along with 'open door policy'.
14 seater charabanc purchased on 3rd January 1923.

1924   Glazing in the Verandahs in the Annexe continues.
New Verandahs added to wards in the main building.

1926   New laundry added.
Gymnasium added to recreation department in the Annexe.
Chapel of rest added to the mortuary (still standing).
Sycamore Farm, Upton, purchased in August.
Radio aerials begin to appear on the roofs throughout the hospital.

1927   Small motor trailer purchased. Vehicles becoming a more frequent site in the hospital grounds.
Construction of tennis courts, badminton and croquet courts adjoining Uplands.

1928   Alterations to farm buildings, including new shippons, sterilisation apparatus and mechanical milking.

1929   Two large water storage tanks of 200,000 gallons capacity completed.
Sewing room in the main hall converted into a dining room.
Shoemakers shop constructed under the Verandah of Male 7 ward.
Swimming pool constructed (recently demolished).

1930   Bowling green completed and 4 acre park.
Occupational therapy building, both sexes completed (recently demolished).

1931-32 Alterations to the main hall including a second projector for the cinema operating room and talking sound film apparatus installed.

1933   Further occupational pavilion provided for male patients (recently demolished).

1934   Male occupational room extended by 120 feet to include, printing book binding room, upholsterers shop, shoemakers shop and tailors shop (recently demolished).

1935   Jam and confectionery room built along with bacon curing room, sausage room, new butchers shop and refrigeration room added. Sewing room also built, all to the west of the main building.
Out-patients clinic established in a room next to Male 3 Ward in the main building.

1936   Rosemount House situated near Field Bank Road adapted as a self care house for female patients without nursing staff.

1937   Hot closets for plates and meals provided in all wards.

New canteen in the main building.

Unsightly telephone lines in the hospital grounds run underground.

1938   16th June work began on the construction of six new villas and a kitchen (since demolished) on land to the west of the original nurses home.

New iron fire escapes added to wards Male 1 and 5 and Female 1 and 5 in the main building.

30th August the purchase of Upton Priory Estate, from the trustees of the late Captain Frankenburgh. 111 acres with buildings for £23,000. Large areas of this converted into market gardens including glasshouse ranges growing a huge range of horticultural produce.

1939   New library formed at the main entrance to the main building.

Entrance hall walls panelled in oak dado.

Annexe used as an Emergency Medical Station for duration of Second World War. 9000 patients passed through in total.

1940   Addition to the original 1902 Nurses' Home completed.

Upton Grange Farm, Upton, and Lower Roewoods Farm, Birtles Road obtained by 'notice to quit'.

Water main extended to Upton Priory Estate.

Assistant Farm Bailiff appointed.

New petrol pump installed under Male 7 ward in the main building.

Various air raid precautions made including the construction of shelters in various parts of the grounds.

Change of name from Cheshire County Mental Hospital to Parkside Hospital.

1941   27th August six 44 bedded villas and a kitchen, along with two villas for medical staff and an extension to the original Nurses' Home, were opened. Hospital patient population increased to 1342.

1942   Further water storage tanks constructed in the parkland with a capacity of 750,000 gallons.

1943   Rosemount Out-Patients Clinic opened along with two early treatment villas.

1946   31st March Emergency Medical Hospital in Annexe closed.

Hospital accommodation restored to 1633 beds.

1947   Dr.P.M.Crowe appointed Medical Superintendent in August (5th Medical Superintendent).

At this time the hospital estate comprised 306 acres.

1948   5th July the **National Health Service** provisions came into being. Parkside became part of the Manchester Regional Health Board and ceased to function as the County Mental Hospital, thus ending 77 years administration at County level. Catchment areas reorganised.

1950s   Deluge of new pharmacological preparations including antipsychotic, antituberculous, anticonvulsant and antibacterial drugs. This marked a major turning point. Populations of the large County Asylums, Tuberculosis Hospitals, Isolation Hospitals and Elderly Care Hospitals start to decline as a result.

Parkside amalgamated with West Park Hospital but still financed and administered separately.

1951   RMPA nursing examinations discontinued. Nursing training school established in old Parkside Isolation Hospital.

1953   Modernisation of the operating theatre in the Annexe which had been in use since 1905.

Deaths of Drs.T.S.Sheldon and H.D.Cormac, 2nd and 4th Medical Superintendents respectively.

1955   Television sets appear on the wards.

1960s   Dr.R.Boardman becomes 6th Medical Superintendent. He was followed by the 7th and last serving Medical Superintendent at Parkside, Dr.J.Littlewood, who retired during the early 1970s.

1966   Industrial therapy unit opens.

1970   Young People's Unit opens.

Parkside merges with Macclesfield and District Group Hospital Management Committee to form the East Cheshire Hospital Management Committee.

Parkside Community Psychiatric Nursing Service formed.

1974   East Cheshire Hospital Management Committee moves from the control of Manchester Regional Health Authority to the Mersey Regional Health Authority. 36 wards open with a total of 989 beds

101 Student nurses and 40 pupil nurses undergoing training at Parkside.

1980s Acceleration of Governmental policy to run down the large County Mental Hospitals.

1982 Parkside becomes part of Macclesfield Health Authority and ceases to have its own financial and administrative control, thus ending 110 years of independence.

1985 Jocelyn Solly House opens.

1991 **'Culture Change'.**
Concept of Purchaser/Provider arrangements.
Formation of Hospital Trusts. Widespread NHS reforms.
Retraction of Parkside continues and it becomes part of the East Cheshire NHS Trust, following a failed bid to become part of a Community Health Unit Trust which is rejected by the Secretary of State.

1992 Business Manager appointed at Parkside.

1993 Macclesfield Health Authority merged with Crewe District Health Authority to become the South and East Cheshire Health Authority (purchasers).
Later merged with Chester to form the South Cheshire Health Authority.

1994 Merger of Mersey Regional Health Authority with the North West Regional Health Authority.

1995 Six wards left at Parkside from a total of 36 in 1974.
22nd September: Last group of patients transferred from the Main Building to the Annexe.
26th September: Original Main Building closed after 5 generations.

1997 **Parkside Hospital closed January 1997**
A new purpose-built mental illness unit of 4 wards called the 'Millbrook Unit' and attached to the Macclesfield District General Hospital was opened at the end of January.

This huge specimen of the horse chestnut near to the medical centre at Parkside Hospital offers peace and quiet.

Bibliography

Brown R (1883) — A Walk Through the Public Institutions of Macclesfield, Page 16.

Bristow G J (undated) — History of Occupational Therapy at Parkside Mental Hospital. Parkside Press.

Batchelor I R C (1969) — Henderson and Gillespies Text Book of Psychiatry. Oxford University Press.

Curl, Prof J S (1990) — Victorian Architecture. London UK. David and Charles.

Crowther MA (1981) — The Workhouse System 1834-1929. Batsford Academic and Educational Ltd.

Flinn M W (1968) — An Economic and Social History of Britain Since 1700. Macmillan and Co.

Hubbard E (1991) — The Work of John Douglas, London, The Victorian Society

Hunter R/MacAlpine I (1963) — Three Hundred Years of Psychiatry 1535-1860, Oxford University Press

Langley M & G (1993) — At the Crossroads. A History of Arclid Workhouse and Hospital, Johnsons of Nantwich.

Longden G (1986) — Life and Labour in Victorian Macclesfield. Neil Richardson.

Oxley G W (1974) — Poor Relief in England and Wales 1601-1834. David and Charles.

Parry-Jones W L (1972) — Trade in Lunacy: A study of Private Madhouses in England in the Eighteenth and Nineteenth Centuries. Routledge and Kegan Paul

Pickstone J.V. (1985) — Medicine and Industrial Society, A History of Hospital development in Manchester and its Region 1752-1946, Manchester University Press.

Pugh P D G (1967) — Practical Nursing. Edinburgh Blackwood.

Pearsall R (undated) — Night's Black Angels. Unknown.

Riley P W G (1966) — A Social and Economic History of England. G Bell and Sons Ltd.

Roberts N (1967) — Cheadle Royal Hospital. A Bicentenary History. John Sherratt and Sons

Siggins G P (1989) — History of West Park Hospital Macclesfield 1939-1948. A W Clowes Ltd.

Wall BA (1977) — A World of its Own. Chester's Psychiatric Hospitals 1829-1976. Cheshire Area Health Authority.

Weatherall N (1986) — Science and the Discovery of Drugs. Seven part series. Pharmaceutical Journal.

Authors, various — Committees' Annual Reports, 1871-1956.
Macclesfield Courier and Herald, Saturday 13 May 1871. Page 5 describes the opening of the Asylum
Department of the Environment Statutory Lists of Buildings.
Pen Pictures of Macclesfield's Public Men. 1907